Edinburgh Review

KU-337-526

EDITOR: BRIAN MCCABE
ASSISTANT EDITOR & PRODUCTION: JENNIE RENTON
REVIEWS EDITOR: MICHAEL LISTER
WEBSITE DEVELOPMENT: Peter Likarish

22a Buccleuch Place
Edinburgh EH8 9LN

edinburgh.review@ed.ac.uk
www.edinburghreview.org.uk

EDITORIAL BOARD: Cairns Craig, Kimberly Hutchings, A.L. Kennedy,
    Andrew O'Hagan

ADVISORY BOARD: Karina Dent, Gavin Miller, Benjamin Morris,
    David Moses

ISSN 0267 6672

Edinburgh Review 119 ISBN 978 1 85933 233 7

© the contributors, 2007

Printed and bound in the UK by the Cromwell Press Ltd,
    Trowbridge, Wiltshire.

Supported by

Scottish
Arts Council

Acknowledgements

The photograph by Kenny Munro on page 5 shows a decorated rickshaw used in the Song of the Rickshaw project.

Many thanks to Sally Harrower of the Manuscripits Division of the National Library of Scotland for information about the Isabella Plumb archive, Acc. 12680; images from the archive are reproduced by kind permission of the Trustees of the National Library of Scotland.

'Arranged Marriage' by Shanta Acharya first appeared in *Numbering Our Days' Illusions* (London: Rockingham Press, 1995) and 'Ganesh Puja', 'Fever in Diwali' and 'Busride to Char Minar' in *Not This, Not That* (India: Rupa & Co., 1994).

Contents

Imminent Ruin and Desperate Remedy: Calcutta and its Fragments

Swapan Chakravorty

Calcutta, by all accounts, is changing. The city now calls itself 'Kolkata', reverting to the demotic variant of 'Kalikata', the name of one of the three villages the Muslim Governor of Bengal sold to the East India Company in 1698. The new name has the sanction of the state, but it has to reckon with the stubborn habits of an amphibious culture. The University of Calcutta, set up in 1857, is in Bengali 'Kalikata Visvavidyalay', and the authorities have failed to make room for the new official name in its formal title in both languages. Calcutta is not an ancient city, not at least by Indian standards, and yet one is none too sure of the etymology of its name. The devout like to believe that it derives from the goddess Kali. Pilgrims, they say, had always flocked to Kalighat, the famous temple on the bank of the old river that, after changing course, is now no wider than a moat. It is one of the fifty-two spots over which the body of Sati (a form of Shakti like Kali herself) was scattered, when Vishnu had to dismember the corpse to stop her enraged husband Siva from destroying the world. In some ways, Calcutta strikes outsiders as having been true to its myth of origin. It is like the orphaned fragment of a lost corpus, for ever caught on the hop between imminent ruin and desperate remedy.

What exactly is it that is changing in the city? West Bengal, the oddly named state on the eastern fringe of the peninsula, was slow to make peace with the market-driven regime that has been steadily dismantling the command economy in India since at least 1989. But the markers of headier times are all in place now, at least in the capital city of the state ruled for close to three decades by a communist-led coalition. New apartment blocks and flyovers tower over an improbable topography and shopping malls are a maze of high-street brands. The small parking lot at my university department, built for the few sad local cars owned mostly by women lecturers with rich husbands, is spilling over with gleaming Japanese, Korean and American models; tabloid celebrities from across the nation drop in on speciality stores and multiplexes; fancy restaurants, lounge bars with ethnic themes and coy night clubs sprout in breathtaking defiance of commercial wisdom; wines take up more shelf-space in liquor-shops while Subway and Pizza Hut try their blandishments on kebab addicts; more children wear ties to school and more parents talk golf and country clubs; fewer upscale hotels offer discounts out of season; stodgy clerks and timid schoolmasters gamble in stocks and mutual funds; electronic betting, now legal, is the new opium of the working class, so are MTV and dating-sites for the young; college celebrations routinely include the models' runway; software geeks and commodity traders work nights; European designers are sprucing up the old airport and the shabby waterfront; the media are noisier against urban eyesores and political strikes; the greenery and open spaces in the city find corporate keepers to scare away tramps and hookers. A slovenly government billboard outside the airport terminal welcomes guests to a 'resurgent' West Bengal. Calcutta, it more than implies, is happening. The city is at last talking money, not talking back to it; and poverty, still too visible, has lost its power to disturb or distract.

A casual visitor, or one returning to the city after several years, will not fail to notice that the city's skyline is changing. As children, we would go up to the terrace of our old three-storeyed block of flats on August afternoons to watch the kites fly. Kite-flying was big in Calcutta at the end of the monsoons, when the skies were clear and the evenings not as short and depressing as they would soon be from late October. After the vacation for Durga Puja and Diwali, one would switch to cricket and swot for the end-of-the-year tests. But the brief spell from August to October would belong to the knights of swooping tetrahedron and to their aerial tournaments in which glistening strings, coated with powdered glass, would graze and tangle. We would wait for the victory chorus to power through the evening air, and then run to grab the felled kite floating gently down, like a leaf in autumn, before it lodged itself on the wireless antennae rearing up from a neighbouring roof. The diamond-shaped specks would loom high above the trees in the east, beyond the Campbell Hospital grounds, reaching as far as the big railway station in

Sealdah. If the wind set in from the east, the flimsy sheets of coloured paper spread on a frame of two intersecting sticks, one straight and the other bent like a bow, would lurch towards the west, and we could spot them against the distant bridge joining the city to the bigger railway terminal across the river in Howrah. The trees are all but gone, and the giant bridge is hidden from view by the concrete mess stretching from one end of Dharmatala Street to the other, right up to the old city centre in Chowringhee.

Some like to call the old city centre Dharmatala. Others call it Esplanade, although the Maidan, the stretch of green that let the British guns at the riverside garrison of Fort William have clear lines of fire, has steadily shrunk, and the civil administration and the army, with corporate help, seem keen to fence off what is left of it. Campbell Hospital is now named after a famous Bengali doctor, and Dharamtala Street is Lenin Sarani. Like the city itself, nearly all its streets and neighbourhoods have more than one name. Unlike the ideologues who pull down statues and rename streets, Calcutta makes little fuss about living simultaneously with its disparate histories.

It is not just the old city centre that is changing. Sturdy and functional office blocks on and around Chowringhee Road (or Jawaharlal Nehru Road), built in the sixties and seventies of the last century, now look like poor shades of a disowned past. The brash condominiums, malls and commercial structures coming up in the southern and eastern fringes of the city have decisively altered the architectural profile, the industrial map and demographic spread. Calcutta grew along the eastern bank of the river the British called the Hooghly. Spreading several miles westward from the old Fort and ringed by moats and ditches, this was the central business district, with government houses, the legislature, the secretariat, the Town Hall, the law-courts and the stock exchange along Esplanade and around the tank in Dalhousie Square. It formed the nucleus of White Town – its elegant clubs, churches, race-course, shops, bars and cemeteries built to cocoon Europeans inside a tenuous shell of familiarity. Further south were the docks in Khidirpur. The port was once cosmopolitan and chaotic, shading off into the Muslim districts where the Nawab of Awadh had taken refuge after being driven away from Lucknow in the middle of the nineteenth century. He brought to the upstart city the grace of a lost world – courtly manners, the elegance of Urdu poetry and song, a lordly cuisine. The descendants of Tipu Sultan, who died fighting the English in 1800, also fled to the city from southern India. The metropolitan culture of Calcutta has always been, in a genuine sense, the culture of the displaced.

Away from the river in the south was the wilderness which provided abundant game, including tigers. Warren Hastings, the Governor General in the eighteenth century whom Edmund Burke famously impeached, had set up his country residence in the area. Close to the gardens of what is now the National Library and the Horticultural Society, he had fought a duel with Philip Francis. The wilderness and the tigers are gone, but the area housed the fringe population of the city until a few years back. One of the two large prisons in the vicinity is now the south campus of Calcutta University. Across from the library and the university is the zoo, built on the sprawling estate of a former maharaja. As children we went there every winter to gaze at the migratory birds from Siberia. Fewer birds take the flight these days: they have not taken kindly to the plush hotel that has come up a few yards away. The neighbourhood now teems with malls, restaurants, speciality hospitals, and the high-walled homes of tycoons, military top brass and civil servants. The zoo, we are told, will soon be shifted: a tiger had killed a drunken man who had entered the enclosure with a garland for the animal just a few years back.

The Black Town was in the north. Bengali landowners, made rich by the East India Company's revenue settlement at the end of the eighteenth century, and an assortment of merchants, agents and clerks from all over the country had built their mansions there in the hybrid architectural idiom of the native arriviste. The old Black Town, stretching to the cremation ground near Baghbazar, has weathered the changes with forlorn sturdiness. The place is still a maze of chaotic bazaars, run-down theatres with mismatched domes, unappetising brothels, job-printers working on treadle machines, night-markets selling used clothes, dreary offices of jatra troupes who make old music and melodrama out of new themes (including Bush and Saddam) on makeshift stages, marching bands on hire that mix fake bassoons with authentic bagpipes, shops for musical instruments such as the sehnai and the sarangi that no one wants to buy, quaint houses of worship built by nineteenth-century religious benefactors and radicals, the earliest academic institutions and libraries, ruined houses with the crest of Queen Victoria moulded on wooden doors, the decayed pretence of chipped stained glass or forsaken fountain featuring Neptune and his sea-horses, eating-houses that live more on memory than custom. Forgotten forms of life cling to north Calcutta with the tenacity of the city's banyan trees, which strike root in concrete pavements, rusted water pipes and crumbling parapets.

Bengalis made money under the British, but lost it to more seasoned business communities of Indians after independence in 1947. The *zamindars* or landlords who collected revenue on behalf of the government were slow to adapt to changing times, and the financial reins of the city have passed to the Marwaris, the Gujaratis and the Punjabis. The better-off among

Bengali professionals began to shift base to the south of the city a couple of decades before independence. The culture of owned apartment housing caught on with salaried Bengalis from the 1960s. Around the same time, the new generation of up-country businessmen started branching off from their ancestral homes in Barabazar and Chitpur in the north. The upscale southern neighbourhoods were the ones least resistant to recent changes, partly because transfer of property was easier here, with legacies, tenancies and entailments being less complicated than in the old family estates of the north. Executives entitled to paid accommodation advertise for flats in the south, since this is where the improvement in urban infrastructure is most visible.

Yet, even after the recent IT boom, the south is not half as cosmopolitan as the north once was. The cultural heterogeneity of the Raj years is still evident in the architectural chaos that is north Calcutta. The official buildings in White Town were mostly neo-Palladian, with a few exceptions such as the High Court, built on the gothic plan of the town hall in Ypres. The Government House, now the residence of the Governor, was modelled after Kedleston Hall, the Derbyshire seat of the Curzons. The churches mostly followed Gibbs's neo-classical style in such exemplars as St Martin's-in-the-Fields in London. This was European Calcutta, the city from which the British governed India from 1774 until the capital was shifted to Delhi in 1912. It was the second city of the empire, which ran the affairs of places as far-off as Rangoon and Melacca. Eighteenth-century paintings of European Calcutta by Thomas Daniell and engravings by William Wood depict spacious buildings with rambling gardens. But as one heads toward the north from Dalhousie Square, one wades into a less tranquil cityscape – a noisy, hybrid, crowded architecture that recalls the heady mix of races and idioms typical of an eighteenth-century port-city. The south, despite its modernist boast, has no Portuguese church. There is no synagogue, and there is no Jain temple built in the style of a Burmese pagoda. Armenian realtors did not invest much in the south, although in 1780 they built a Greek church with Doric columns there. The old mansions of Black Town speak of the contradictions of a modernity under colonial rule – a courtyard facing the open porch raised on antique columns for pujas and other ceremonies, the front quarters flaunting European-style parlours and billiard rooms, the more traditional quarters at the back housing the women, who could watch a ceremony or a theatrical performance from behind bamboo slats on the first-floor galleries. Then there are the haveli-style houses of rich Muslims with Persian tracery; there were the ornate lattice-work and embossed windows in the Rajasthani houses built by Marwaris. The promise of modernity in the north, though compromised by the colonial presence, was promiscuous and inclusive; it is ironic that 'postmodernity' in the south should threaten homogeneity and exclusion.

Black Town was slow to urbanise. In the middle of the eighteenth century, it was still a confusion of hovels, alleyways and gutters. After more than 250 years, hand-pulled rickshaws and carts are more abundant in the north. That, however, did not impair its ethnic variety. Even crime was multinational. On 29 January 1795, a band of 200 robbers attacked the house of a rich Bengali, Chaitanya Seal. The house was in the north, in Kasipur (Cossipore). The gang included Italians, Portuguese, Frenchmen, Germans and Bengalis. Portuguese bandits joined Bengalis in storming the house of Chaitanya Datta in Coolootolla on 21 October 1789.

There were, it is true, Portuguese, Dutch, French and Danish settlements within a few miles of the city. However, discrete histories of urbanisation are known to breed their own kinds of ethnic mix. The Chinese arrived in Calcutta around 1780. They made sugar out of the cane they grew: the Bengali word for sugar is *chini*. Although many were forced to leave the country following the Sino-Indian war in 1962, the Chinese population in the city exceeded 20,000 around 1980. Most of the settlers worked in the leather factories in the eastern fringe, where they built a walled neighbourhood named Tangra. The leather workshops have been shifted out of town, but the Chinese restaurants in Tangra are doing well. Iranian dissidents smuggled seditious tracts out of Calcutta, a distinguished centre of Persian printing in the nineteenth century. The Baghdadi Jews and Armenians were still around when I went to school. It was a Methodist institution, where several Jewish teachers and students sang in the school choir. They had names like David and Isaac, and we used to confuse them with the Anglo-Indians. In any case, there was no difference in their enthusiasm for Cliff Richard numbers which, for some reason still dark to me, followed the hymns at 'chapel' hour. The Armenians played rugby in the local league. We would feel bullied by the Armenian school teams in hockey and football: they were big boys who believed every sport in the world was rugby. I had no idea that the novelist Thackeray had lived in the house that was then the Armenian school. We were also scared of the turbaned Afghans, in loose shirts that reached down to their knees and baggy pleated salwars. They would prowl outside factory gates on pay-day, and we heard chilling rumours of how these loan-sharks – Kabuliwallahs, we called them – forced defaulters to part with their month's wages. Did they have families here? Not visible ones. *Kabuliwallahar bou* (Kabuliwallah's wife) is Bengali for something one knows is there but never gets to see. Nepalis took up domestic jobs and Bhutanese women set up roadside stalls to sell cheap woollens.

Indians came all over. Every winter Kashmiri men came in droves to sell shawls. Gujaratis and Sindhis owned commercial establishments. The Sikhs from Punjab drove and repaired commercial vehicles, sold automobile parts, managed roadside eateries known as *dhabas* and were the best carpenters. Marathis and Tamils, employed in banks, mercantile houses and schools, formed strong cultural organisations. The poor from the neighbouring states of Bihar, Assam and Orissa filled the big demand for industrial labour and the bigger one for unskilled manual work. I never got to learn about the ethnic mosaic in the sex-trade.

The cultural mix began to change in the 1960s. The border-war in 1962 drove out many Chinese families; the easing of immigration laws encouraged Anglo-Indian families to leave for Australia or Canada and Jewish families for Israel; government banks and welfare schemes checked the Afghan money-lenders; Belgian Jesuits were slowly replaced by the Indians they had trained in their seminaries; the British who had stayed back found it hard to socialise with the new crowd at the clubs. There were more people on the streets: the railway platforms were spilling over with refugees from East Pakistan and migrant labourers from the neighbouring states. By 1974, the population had swollen to 3.3 million (the official count is now close to 11.5 million). But there were fewer Eurasian chefs and crooners in the restaurants on Park Street; fewer jockeys on the race-course spoke the Anglo-Indian idiom that had so amused Naipaul; rugby was an orphaned sport. Ungainly Landmasters and Ambassadors, the passenger cars manufactured by Hindustan Motors, had taken over the roads from the stately Austins, Wolseleys and Plymouths. The statues of British governors and soldiers were stowed away, and street-names were changed. Foreign looks and accents, like foreign cars, were fast becoming a curiosity. Calcutta was no longer the first-born city of colonial India; White Town wore a derelict look.

Lazy journalists and pedlars of literary nostalgia routinely blame communists and their militant trade-unions for the flight of capital from Bengal since the 1960s. The communists now in power seem to have bought this line. They regret 'past mistakes', and seize every imaginary occasion to assure investors that they have changed their spots. Life would have been simpler had they been such overpowering agents of history. Calcutta started slipping well before the communists tasted power. The Second World War put a halt to the influx of capital goods, the Japanese bombed Calcutta, famine killed more than four million in Bengal in 1943–44, the stock markets crashed in the wake of the sectarian riots in 1946. Sectarian violence in the 1940s started the pattern of displacements that assumed disastrous proportions when Bengal was partitioned in 1947. More than six million refugees from East Pakistan migrated to Calcutta and the adjoining districts in the next two decades. As late as 1969, 1.3 million refugees were officially awating rehabilitation in the state. Not all of them waited that long. Refugees forcibly took hold of land in and around Calcutta, sometimes fighting pitched battles with landowners for months. Pressure on land meant a lateral spread of shops and slums, with drastic change in the demographic lay-out. Shanty-towns now housed former middle-class householders and farmers; the civic administration and amenities were on the verge of collapse.

The war with Pakistan in 1965 resulted in a suspension of the Five-Year Plan, with consequent drying up of funds from the federal government. Ancillary industries dependent on orders from government departments such as the railways, started laying off workers. Jute, ceramic, chemical, textile and engineering industries in the state were already facing the effects of obsolescence: the depreciated units were passing into the hands of asset-strippers. Food was scarce all over India in the late 1960s. The government in West Bengal imposed sale restrictions on farmers to ensure supplies in ration shops, and cordoned off villages to check the smuggling of grains into the blackmarket in Calcutta. Social arrangements in the villages were soon unsettled. Thousands of women who had never been out working swarmed into the smuggling trade, boarding commuter trains with pitiful bundles of rice hidden in the folds of their saris. Shanty towns sprang up along the smugglers' route, flanking railway tracks and canals, and the jobless and the homeless squatted on the city's pavements.

The elections in 1967 brought communists to power as partners in an unsteady coalition. The state-sponsored unrest in agriculture and industry that followed was bound to prove ineffectual. Food prices rose, factories closed down, corporate houses moved their head offices to other metros. Disaffected revolutionaries left the mother party to join the Maoist movement that began with the peasant uprising in Naxalbari, a hitherto obscure village in the north of the state. 1968 was a heady year not just for Europe. The Maoists in Bengal launched a guerilla movement, and otherwise qualmish young men killed policemen and died on the streets of Calcutta. State reprisals turned more brutal with the return of the Congress party to power in 1972. The surrender of the Pakistani army and the birth of Bangladesh in 1971 had turned Indira Gandhi into a popular icon. Nevertheless, the party chose to rig the elections, and the hoods they commissioned joined crime and politics in a lasting bond. When Mrs Gandhi declared the Emergency in 1975 and suspended fundamental rights, the protests in Calcutta were strangely muted. Counter-culture seemed to have learnt its lessons. Mrs Gandhi called elections to Parliament in 1977, and the constitutional Marxists joined forces in West Bengal with right-wing parties. Secure in its mastery of the sly art of electioneering, the left won the Bengal elections on their own soon after. They have never lost an election in Bengal since.

The instability and police terror in the decade following 1967 had crippling consequences for trade and the service sector. Shops and restaurants were deserted in the evenings; offices of international airlines closed down; hotels looked like bleak retreats for the moneyed fugitive. In the early seventies, when I was at the university, examinations were never held on time. There was this co-curricular innovation newspapers termed 'mass-copying', and no one bothered to employ a graduate from Calcutta. No one bothered to invest in the city's infrastructure. The port was left to die a natural death, roads were a nightmare, sewers were choked, phones seldom worked, hospitals and factories had no electricity for hours.

Even then, Calcutta never meant trouble and Mother Teresa, not at least for us. There was more passion in the air than blood in the streets. The rhetoric of austerity, the tetchy intolerance of trivia, the moralist suspicion of money, and the cultural snobbery with which one associates the Calcutta psyche now look like hypocritical alibis for economic failure. But that failure taught Calcutta to make bricks without straw. Universities bred world-class scholars in dingy labs and unlit libraries. Literature was desperately bold in a city without professional authors. Amateur theatre groups produced the finest classics of Indian theatre in mouldering playhouses and the studios in Tollygunge shot amazing films on rationed raw stock with the shoddiest of equipment. My father used to camp through the night outside packed marquees to catch the strains of the classical concerts inside. I have seen demure women in saris climb trees to steal a glimpse of the open-air stage on the birth anniversary of Rabindranath Tagore. In a sense, this was predictable. The flawed promise of colonial modernity had schooled Calcutta into configuring a nation its people were denied: the city had then learned to invent nation as cultural idea. When Calcutta lost its grip on the levers of the national economy, it fell back on this legacy of material self-denial and cultural creativity. Political action and cultural vanguardism in the 1960s and 1970s were the perverse responses of the city robbed of economic agency. The communists – not the Maoist fringe but those in Parliamentary politics – consolidated that process into political dividends; they cannot be said to have created it.

The peculiar conditions of urban growth in Calcutta, as also the paucity of civic infrastructure, gave a festive openness to the city's culture and politics.

Life, disease and death have always been more visible in Calcutta than in any other city of comparable size and importance. Western visitors often fail to make sense of this visibility, attributing it to poverty and homelessness. People who live on pavements are not the only ones who live out their private lives in the open, nor are they necessarily homeless or jobless. Those with jobs and homes may be sleeping rough, washing themselves or their clothes at the roadside water-spouts. Vendors of street food cook and clean on the streets. Drivers and rickshaw pullers spend nights on vehicles parked on the road, and perfectly respectable men think nothing of relieving themselves behind idle lorries. Children play cricket on the road; shirtless elders chat sitting on the front deck of their houses. Death is a visible event. Even a few years back, most corpses of Hindus were carried on the shoulders of men who chanted God's name in chorus like jubilant cheerleaders, and cremation workers celebrated death in the family by taking the hearse out in a procession led by happy drummers. Wedding processions can be boisterous, with drums and crackers shaking up the neighbourhood. In old-fashioned Punjabi and Bihari weddings, bystanders gather to catch a glimpse of the turbaned groom before the bride has set eyes on him.

White Town and its privileged enclaves were built on the principle of exclusion: exclusion of the troublesome native, of the chaos, noise and filth that marked the life of the imperfectly urbanised workforce. Black Town treated urban space as an inclusive arena, a space that merged the civic with the intimate. The resultant attitude to public space has spread to more genteel sections of civil society in many Indian cities. In Calcutta, the moral regimen of the family blended seamlessly into community surveillance. The elders of the neighbourhood would come down heavily on a young man trying out a cigarette or chatting up a girl, and more often than not his parents would approve. The delinquent could count on the same officious guardians to help out with the catering at his wedding, to arrange for an ambulance when his parents were ill, or to carry them on their shoulders when they were dead.

Calcutta's cultural life will appear puzzling unless one understands this rare phenomenon of the urban commons. Hawkers occupy the pavements; cots for the dead are sold outside hospital gates and bookstalls block one's view of the university campus on College Street; migrant workers reproduce villages in miniature under flyovers; mud huts are built with the earth shovelled up from construction sites. The city is a daze of incredible structures during festivals – usually made of plywood and bamboo and cloth – that simulate old palaces and temples, or even the Eiffel Tower and the Library of Congress. On certain days, such as Holi and Muharram, traffic is suspended and the roads are taken over by ceremonial processions. Every occasion spawns a fair. The book fair draws about 800,000 people, and it was amusing to hear a clueless Jacques Derrida lament the demise of the book while inaugurating it a few years back. In the winter months, there are literary fairs, art fairs, music fairs, culture fairs, food fairs, trade fairs, garment fairs, leather fairs, tourism fairs, technology fairs. There is no permanent fairground, the sprawling Maidan being the usual location for these carnivals. Every inch of civic space – roads, parks, gardens – is makeshift space, just as every inch of private space is communal space. The block of flats where I live is lit up during Durga Puja by people I vaguely know. The entrance to the house on these days is crowded with late-night revellers, hawkers and beggars; the drummers sleep on the stairs before being asked.

The left could in the past mobilise the displaced – refugees, squatters, illegal tenants, hawkers, the homeless – with spectacular success partly because of this attitude to public space. Infringement of civic laws bred an incongruous claim to legitimacy. Forcible occupation of private property or public roads and illegal electrical connections were ways in which the more recent variants of Black Town would resist exclusion. The undivided Communist Party had used the conditions without much fuss. They would sell books by Lenin and Ché Guevara at a discount outside the venues of religious festivals. They also used to organise a cultural festival in the cricket stadium at the Eden Gardens. At one such event, I had my first experience of a film by Satyajit Ray. I was eight years old. Bored by the literary seminars and the high-brow plays elsewhere in the stadium, I sat on the grass scorched by the spikes of dreaded fast bowlers, while *Aparajito* (*The Unvanquished*), the sublime chronicle of our modernist moment, unfolded on a crumpled screen raised on bamboo stilts. The show was free, but such pleasures came at a price. Processions and meetings still paralyse life on weekdays. Election campaigns are like violent festivals, and no one asks your permission before painting slogans on your walls. If you are marked out by fate for such things, you might just lose your garage to the election agents.

The underground railway in the 1980s and satellite television in the 1990s were early signals of the recent changes. The metro joined the north of the city to the south in what was more than a symbolic link. Outsiders wonder why the same citizens who do not worry too much about garbage and traffic rules, change their habits when they climb down to the metro stations. Confronted with a space outside social locations, a city without skies, they behave like docile tourists, queueing up behind the barriers and anxiously searching for litter bins. Supermarkets today cause a similar disorientation. Gone are the familiar demarcations – Hindu butchers selling goat-meat in sections where beef-stalls had no entry; Muslims taking up stalls of dry fruits, vermicelli and eggs at a distance; the Chinese selling pork and bacon from allotted sheds beyond the market precincts. The divisions are now subtler, invisible, driven by hardnosed commercial sense. Satellite television had a different kind of levelling effect. Bengalis now watch pretty much the same programmes that Biharis and Punjabis do. Earnest housewives watch American soaps, and no one climbs trees to watch a Tagore opera.

Now that the city has to adjust to the global market, the communists find themselves saddled with the ironic task of imposing the orderly claims of civil society against the carnival of the fringe. The old industrial map has changed with the dismantling of the protectionist economy. The premises of defunct factories are being handed over to developers who build condominiums, malls and multiplexes. The patriarchal communitarianism of the neighbourhood has no place in these new enclaves. The fishermen of the eastern suburbs have moved out, with developers buying up every available piece of land flanking the eastern bypass. Derelict warehouses along the river may soon be converted into Singapore-style restaurants. The High Court has banned political processions and meetings on weekdays; crackers and microphones are illegal; the Election Commission has outlawed political graffiti. Communists now plead with their own trade unions to ignore the workforce in information technology so that American clients are not upset. The government has tried, with fitful success, to evict squatters and hawkers. The court and the army have ordered that messy fairs be moved out of the Maidan. The primary task of the civic authorities now seems to be restricting access to public space and carefully licensing its use. The Maidan itself is being fenced off, and one has to pay a fee to walk in the gardens of the Victoria Memorial.

The culture of new Calcutta is struggling to find alternative room for the carnival and the forum. If it fails – and all signs say it will – the city will be the last to capitulate to the 'liberal' logic underlying the empire. It was the same empire that had given birth to Calcutta, and to the cosmopolitan promise it was powerless to keep.

The City That Writers Built

Anjana Basu

Calcutta seems to have a strange effect on writers. Considering that the city was built by East India Company commerce, a race of account-tallying soldiers who called themselves writers, the effect is far from surprising. The fertile soil of the delta, which was perfect breeding ground for commerce, also inspires floods of words that grow green and tall and spatter the walls and the political processions. One frustrated writer despairing of finding any other canvas for his art wrote 'the earth goes four million times around the sun' over and over again on fire hydrants and post boxes until death put an end to his effusions.

This persistence was an aspect of the Bengali that the British empire particularly despised, Lord Curzon commenting on an intellect comparable to that of the ancient Greeks and a moral fibre that matched a rabbit's. Look around and you will find the wall loungers and the tea shop crowders who have seemingly nothing better to do than indulge in adda, conversations that take into account happenings all over the world ranging from Castro's eightieth birthday speech to Zidane's head-butting antics. Adda is both the life and death of Calcutta – it fires its literary spirit and runs its commerce into the ground. Something that the city's thirty-year-old rulers, the Marxists, are gradually beginning to realise.

Every celebrity visitor to the city stands up in front of his or her audience and declares glibly that Calcutta has an inexhaustible wealth of culture, fronted by the mighty Colossus of Rabindranath Tagore. Gunter Grass spent a year in the city and battled his revulsion at the abject poverty, which hit him in the eye while marvelling at what he called the throbbing vibrancy, the determination to survive despite overwhelming odds. '*Kolkata cholchey cholbey*, Calcutta is moving and will continue to move', that is the slogan of the city. Never mind the fact that the city seems to move like a slothful juggernaut at the best of times.

The whole thing spirals off into another endless debate about who said what and who was right. Usually the Calcuttan, because a city that boasts two Bengali Nobel Prize winners can never be wrong. Four Bengalis is an adda says one much publicised joke on the internet and even if it isn't Bengalis, any group in Calcutta can spin a literary discussion, as I found one summer.

That was a strange summer, a girl just out of college rushed into a room filled with piles of books wrapped in pinks, yellows and greens with threadwork borders stolen from cotton saris, dominated by a thin white candle of a man. The girl was myself and that was my first bewildered introduction to the literary scene of Calcutta. I had written a book of poems in English and it had been published in that exotic sari wrapping, pink in my case, a bright shriek of a book like a summer flower. There were others besides the tall man in that room, jostling for space between the books. Indo Anglian literature they called it, a term that I had never heard before, and all at once I was part of a fraternity.

It was called Writer's Workshop and the man who headed it, Professor P. Lal, had invented the term Indo Anglian to describe Indian writing in English. Lal broke ground by publishing Vikram Seth when no other publisher in India would touch him. The group of writers met every Sunday morning in Lal's library and discussed the world and new writing in what I came to discover was typical Calcutta adda style.

Get together somewhere, a stoep in the neighbourhood will do, and talk poetry, politics and culture. Arguments fuelled by cups of hot sweet tea and samosas or on a white sheet in a large room or a garden on a Wednesday evening, the way the writer Samar Sen used to hold them in a legendary time. The organised literary addas are now few and far between, because finding a place to hold them has become difficult – these things need a sound system, food and a generous sponsor to pay for it all. A few groups who have introduced the subscription system still hold out, but it must be confessed, stimulating beverages, gossip and high-minded ideas float more freely than brilliant output.

Inspired by the term Indo Anglian and those Sunday morning meetings,

I began a series of light-hearted researches into Indian writing in English and discovered certain things that startled me. For example, the first book in English by an Indian was a novel called *Rajmohan's Wife,* written by Bengal's answer to Sir Walter Scott, Bankimchandra Chatterjee in the nineteenth century. He gave up the attempt after that and reverted to Bengali, becoming the father of the Bengali novel. The poet Michael Madhusudan Dutta experimented with the blank verse form and after several false starts in English proceeded to introduce it to Bengali again. Stanzas from his epic poem 'The Slaying of Meghnad' continue to plague inky-fingered children in examination papers – blank verse loses much of its charm when wrestling with School Final Bengali. And then, of course, there was Tagore who crowned it by being the first Indian, not to mention Bengali, to win the Nobel Prize for Literature.

Calcutta to a woman sings Tagore in many kinds of melodies, though mercifully does not write him. Tagore was fluent enough in English to translate his *Gitanjali,* but gave rise to a school of worshipping translators who perpetuated the myth of the word for word translation, whether it sounded like poetry or not.

Certainly, English at that point raised eyebrows in academic circles – there was a feeling that those students who wrote well in English were using their language to distract examiners from their essential lack of knowledge. My own Ph.D thesis fell on that battlefield – my guide a doyen of Calcutta University quietly advised me to rewrite it because it was 'too entertaining'.

Calcutta has contradictory sources of inspiration. When all the names of the streets were being changed from those commemorating the East India Company lord sahibs and Governors General, Theatre Road found itself being rechristened Shakespeare Sarani. After many debates the Corporation had decided that the road's theatrical associations could still be preserved in the new name – and Shakespeare, after all is not for an age but for all time. Hungerford Street, somewhat later along the way, succumbed to the trend and became Picasso Bithi.

With the passing of time, I came to realise that English writing was in retreat from Calcutta, mainly because of the communist revolution that had swept the city in the seventies. The Marxist stranglehold had effectively caused industry to flee West Bengal and cut a swathe through the job market. As a result, writers like Shashi Tharoor saw no reason to return to the city they had grown up in and found themselves name and fame in other parts of the world. The centre of English publishing relocated to Delhi and began expanding by leaps and bounds.

Where Marxism choked English, it nurtured a garden of writers who talked about comparing the full moon to a singed piece of toast and other equally surreal fantasies. To a man they worked for a living. I ran into the Bengali novelist Shankar, one of the most popular of them, when having abandoned academe and sold myself to advertising, I found an agency designing covers for his novels. A practical man, Shankar earned his daily bread as a public relations officer for Dunlop India Limited before that industrial giant downed its shutters. In corporate circles Manishankar Mukherjee is still a name to reckon with, while in literature he has moved from novels of Calcutta's social life to a book on the food habits of the Bengali. But then, except for Samaresh Basu, few Bengali writers have believed in devoting their lives to the full-time creation of fiction. Even Sunil Gangopadhyay used to work in a newspaper office, planning pages and checking proofs and saving his creative efforts for the weekends.

Of course this state of affairs mysteriously changes come September or October. Every year in autumn, just before Durga Puja, the Bengali magazines publish fat annuals swelled by the new works from the names in the literary sphere. The publishers woo the novelists for new works every year. And if the writer in question wants to produce a fifty-page novella to meet the deadline he is forced to resort to desperate measures. Like a 'do not disturb' notice put on an office door after lunch and the word of mysterious meetings spread around. That period of seclusion never fails to produce a work that will gratify the annual readers and one that perhaps later will be magnified to produce a full length novel or a serial on TV and a stage adaptation.

Theatre was alive and kicking, Rudraprasad Sengupta directing seminal productions like *Antigone* and *Football* (an adaptation of Peter Terson's *Jigger Jagger*). It was the time of the social message delivered with a swift kick to the jaw through experimental stagecraft, some of it kitchen sink drama in the best Wesker style. I remember watching chapatis being rolled onstage in one of the plays, *Bound by Responsibility*, dough round after dough round in a world surrounded by gloom and truck tyres.

'You have no soul,' said my rebel friends. 'You can't even read Bengali.' That was not strictly true – I had been one of those children wrestling with ink and calligraphy and had gone through a steady diet of the great nineteenth-century novelists of Bengal, the ones who had laid the foundations for this present-day Calcutta. The layer that comprised Saratchandra Chatterjee whose down to earth stories still inspire Bollywood filmmakers, Kaji Nasrul Islam, Bonophool, Premendra Mitra who wrote detective fiction or Parsuram who wrote some of the funniest short stories ever, under his enigmatic pen name. Political protests, demands for freedom – they were all there in many of those works in uncompromising black and white.

Calcutta is lucky that very few of its writers suffer from bans or oppression – the prevailing climate of opinion is as happy go lucky as the city. The late great Shakti Chattopadhyay, who was always making news for kissing a police officer at midnight after he'd been arrested for brawling, actually went to court to declare that he was setting a good example to the younger generation by foreswearing all kinds of pleasures except for fruit juice. He was the one whom Allen Ginsberg had inducted into LSD in the early sixties on a stray visit to India. In the days before Page 3 'Shaktida' stood for the odd combination of bohemianism and brouhaha that was very typically intellectual Calcutta.

Here women writers share the limelight shoulder to shoulder with the men. A woman novelist in her younger days, as the wife of an IAS officer, used to spend days and nights with the tribals in Bihar in an attempt to discover the essential realism of Santhali culture. Another briefly caught the attention of a French film unit with the story of her affair with a visiting Romanian engineer in the 1930s. It had the Bengali aunts murmuring under their white veils for quite a while since the lady in question had by then attained white-veiled status. Ashapurna Devi during her lifetime was awarded the Jnanpith Award for her trilogy on the experience of being a woman.

Taslima Nasreen, hounded by her home government after she wrote *Shame*, was frequently to be encountered at consulate parties and clubs, even though several years later, in a fit of sudden empathy with the Muslim lobby, the Buddhadeb Bhattacharya government astounded her by banning *Split in Two*. The ban cast a shadow over Bengal's literary open mindedness and was of course removed soon after the High Court intervened, but while it lasted there was a spate of meetings and addas.

A recent publishing deal between France and India has allowed Bengali works to be translated into French and vice versa. At the book fair, that annual meeting ground for minds, I heard the Bengali version of one of Jean Genet's novels being read aloud. The launch was also used as a platform for affirming gay solidarity in Bengal – gays had apparently been banned from promoting their poetry at another smaller book fair in Chandanagar. To put the two things together seemed relevant given Genet's unconventional take on morality and combining it with the fact that Chandanagar had originally been built by the French, spearheading their imperial aims in India.

The book fair is possibly Kolkata's most lauded literary event. That is the time when the Publishers' Guild sets up its marquees and stalls and the intelligentsia of the city stroll through the sprawling fairgrounds exchanging gossip and literature. If there is a book to be launched, the book fair is the place to do it, even though, in the middle of all that noise, it is sometimes difficult to hear what is being said – unless like the Genet translators you happen to boast an air-conditioned pavilion. The book fair has an adda centre, a place for exchanging leaflets, and anyone who can command a podium and a microphone can get to his feet and talk literature to the air. Every year the Book Fair chooses a country to pay tribute to – Spain and France have been so honoured over the last few years. Delegates and authors from these countries sometimes come to mingle with the local writers and the Government officials. If you survive the jostling and station yourself at a central point you are quite likely to find the luminaries of the literary scene hurrying past you like Alice's White Rabbit, neatly starched dhotis clutched in one hand.

Now the city is acquiring another kind of identity by associating itself with the South Asian diaspora. Shashi Tharoor and Amitav Ghosh, one brought up here, one a Bengali, are prime names. As is Amartya Sen, of course, the other Bengali Nobel Prize winner, who turns out economic dissertations that, while they may not be literary, will stimulate conversations in the cocktail party circuit. Günter Grass arrives to discuss his diary *Show Your Tongue*, a take off on the goddess Kali from whom the city supposedly got its name. The name of course started another endless debate in 2001 when the city's intelligentsia decided after much thought that if Peking could become Beijing, Calcutta had a right to become Kolkata. Sunil Gangopadhyay spearheaded that controversy declaring that the city's integrity had to be restored. The point was whose integrity was it anyway? Calcutta the city had a legend and a name whether it was derided, sighed over or wooed. Kolkata as Kolkata still has to make its mark even though it is trying hard.

The second-hand-book-crammed bylanes of College Street, known as the 'book neighbourhood' to every Bengali, are being organised into a mall. The limp kurta clad young men with embroidered Shan bags hanging from their shoulders who stalked these streets are reinventing themselves in 'jean pants' and mobile phones, while the old handset Puja specials have been digitised. Kolkata has new toys to play with unlike the late lamented Calcutta. At the same time, it is a poor neighbour of Delhi or Mumbai – the literati of the other cities just about recognise it. Writer's Workshop which first taught me the literary world is a shadow of its old glory – more commercial publishers of English writing have sprung up. Amit Chaudhuri's is the only internationally recognised English writing name in the city, but dig hard enough and the Kolkata fraternity will turn up relatives everywhere; Arundhati Roy's cousin, for example, a retiring girl with shy literary ambitions who materialised as a relative of a friend – that is part of the kind of creepers and family tree convolution that Calcutta literary society rejoices in.

There are more Bengali works being translated into English – recently Baby Halder, a maid, wrote her autobiography, something which would have been unthinkable before. Joy Goswami is making a name in poetry, an infusion of relatively young blood to compensate for Sunil Gangopadhyay who recently celebrated his seventieth birthday with an outpouring of romantic verse. Alka Saraogi is winning awards for her novels in Hindi, backed by her own translations.

The future seems to be promising and the conveyor belt production line of Bengali writing continues unabated. If you think that this is too commercial, remember that there is a trend that has been noticed time and time again. A period of relative commercial inanity or mediocrity is suddenly broken by something inspired – Bimal Kar's *Deowad* or Ramapada Chowdhury's *Kharij*. Or a Jibananda Das protesting against the Tagorean influence with his sensuous word play and the influences of Eliot and Whitman.

Despite everything, despite the strikes, *bandhs*, protests or stagnation that characterise it, the soil of the Ganges delta produces a climate that will not kow-tow to the every day or the ordinary. Whether Calcutta or Kolkata, it is, after all, the city built by writers.

As I Saw Kolkata Changing

Bashabi Fraser

Early in the morning in the fresh light of a Kolkata waking up to another day, a missive from the world outside, curled and wound by a jute string would come spinning and then glide through the open door onto our red cement floor. It never missed its target – one open door of many others on the second floor of a *jhul baranda*, a hanging verandah. I always ran out to peer through the trellis work of our wrought iron railing to see the newspaper man cycling away and stopping every so often to throw his next missile with the sure aim of a champion bowler, an art he must have picked up playing cricket in the numerous lanes or *para*,[1] parks of the metropolis.[2]

And that is the memory of my childhood view of Kolkata, looking across a street of buildings similar to ours, with three and four storeys of ornate balconies and French windows with green wooden shutters, the bottom sections of which I could reach and lift the wooden levers to open on sleepy afternoons, to capture a glimpse of the vendors, like the one who twanged his one-stringed instrument, lugging his gunny bag of cotton wool, as he raised his nasal singsong voice to ask for *lep toshok*, quilts and mattresses. He could then rip these open on our terrace, releasing a hundred soft feathery cotton tufts that he twanged into softer recycled buoyancy for renewed winter comfort.

But this swirl of feathery delight could not match the magic of the fifty pigeons we had in the *chilekotha*[3] on the terrace, housed in a custom made

26

dovecote from where our neighbour, Notonda[4], would lift them up, having fed them earlier, and then send them surging across the sky, free to roam till he called them back in a ritual of homecoming, before every sunset.

This was the same terrace whose walled divisions I would be able to cross when I was a little older, after we came back to Kolkata from a three year trip away, to stretch a paper kite on a sharpened string, with which we raced backwards and flung up and then went back to retrieve the manipulating string from a companion, to feel the excitement of a competitive game played without scruples as we schemed to let our kite reign while we cut the life line of other kites, a tribe of colourful participants in Kolkata's skies. This sky was also visible from an inner verandah which ran round the block on the inside, as the whole house was built round an open courtyard in the middle and all the upper floors looked down into it. It was an Anglo-Indian and Bengali Christian neighbourhood, a remnant of British India.

The capital of British India, from 1772 till 1911/12, Kolkata celebrated its tercentenary in 1990. It still retains many of the national assets of India, such as the Asiatic Society of India,[5] the National Library,[6] the Indian National Museum,[7] the Victoria Memorial Museum and Calcutta University,[8] which was India's first modern university and today has around 200 affiliated colleges.

There are many buildings in Kolkata that are reminders of its British legacy, many of which stand round what was once called Dalhousie Square, now known as B.B.D. Bag, prominent amongst which are the government secretariat, the massive redbrick Writers' Building and the General Post Office with its distinctive dome.[9] There is St Paul's Cathedral beside the newer Academy of Fine Arts, the gothic Kolkata High Court near the Strand and the Governor's Palace which would have fitted the old description of Kolkata as the 'City of Palaces', a world one can still recall if one takes a launch/steamer ride along the Hugli, to witness the grand edifices that line the river, behind which the urban sprawl continues undeterred. Kolkata is also the city of colonial style clubs, where liveried waiters make the populous city fade amidst this manicured luxury. In fact, the Tollygunge Golf Club[10] (one of the three golf courses in Kolkata), is where Bob Wright and his wife stayed, keeping Anglo-India alive, as Mr Wright remained managing member from 1972 till 1977 and continued to live at what he affectionately called the 'Tolly', till he died in April 2005.

Then there are the old mansions, like the ones at Park Circus and Esplanade, which have still not been axed by developers' schemes. Some of these mansions and old houses in Kolkata bear witness to Kolkata's cosmopolitan inclusiveness, a story that is told in its Armenian Street, its Greek Orthodox Church, its Chinese restaurants, beauty parlours and hairdressers, its Anglo-Indian schools, its Parsi and Irani businesses and its Tibetan refugees.

Looking back at the end of the fifties, I wonder, was Kolkata quieter then? We could hear the clanging of the trams on the main road which ran parallel to our street. We lived in a sort of joint family. Not the usual patriarchal one of a father's family home, but one forced by circumstances on my young working parents, which was not uncommon in the mid-fifties of Kolkata. Partition had drawn a border overnight and many found their family homes and land on the 'other' side. These were the new migrants of Kolkata and they came in an unending stream, extending the city's boundaries beyond its built-up north and central blocks, to settle and build on the swampy land, much of it rice fields, south of the city. I realise now how lucky we were, that my parents found lecturing jobs and were able to provide a home for their siblings in our small flat. So I had uncles and aunts from both my father's and mother's side staying with us, spoiling me as the only child in the family. My uncles and aunts were all studying and doing little jobs to keep the 'family' going.

But there were other families who were not so fortunate. With no government plan to rehabilitate the refugees, those who came pouring into Shealdah Railway station, languished for years on the platforms, whole families living their meagre, undignified lives amidst a metropolis which, since then, has been struggling to cope with its population of around 14 million in its urban agglomeration which covers 1750 sq. km, though its Municipal Corporation area is only 185 sq. km. Kolkata is a north-south sprawl, a port on the eastern bank of the Hugli river in the Indo-Gangetic delta, comprised of alluvial soil and flanked by wetlands on the east, much of which has been reclaimed. Many of the East Pakistan refugees were supporters of Netaji Subhas Bose and were initially suspicious of the Communist Party which had sided with the war effort of the British Government and was considered anti-Subhas. Moreover, the refugees were wary of offending the post-Independence Congress government of West Bengal, still hoping for rehabilitation succour from it. But when the latter proved elusive, they organised themselves under communist leadership and illegally occupied abandoned barracks and land with tacit government support, right up to Dum Dum and Barrackpore in the north and Tollygunge, Jadabpur and Garia in the south, in the squatters' colonies that changed the face of Kolkata and its politics forever.

Then began the bitter struggle against the establishment as eviction procedures and orders were fought in protracted legal battles, protest demonstrations and rallies were organised, arrests courted in a game of survival. The state government's initial disinterest in the refugees, in spite of their sizeable numbers, was probably because they did not have a voting right. Once this right was established, these squatters' colonies became the hot point of political angling, as agitational politics became the order of the Kolkata political scene and left party coalitions were voted into power in short-lived state governments in 1967 and 1969, till a communist government was elected in 1977 and has since been re-elected again and again, marking the left, radical thinking of Kolkata as entrenched and almost unalterable.

This is the same left thinking that organised the Hindu-Muslim tram workers to hold a united front in a long strike agitating for workers' rights in the face of communal violence that ripped the city apart in 1946. And in this same city, tram-burning crowds protest against the existing establishment from time to time. Kolkata remains the only city in India with trams, introduced in 1902, which meander through its six per cent road surface area. I remember what a treat it was to be taken by my aunts and uncles on winter weekends for a tram ride to the Victoria Memorial gardens, before the mist had lifted from the Maidan, the green heart of Kolkata.[11] On the way, I was fascinated by the hydrants at work, oozing water from hundreds of spouts, washing the city clean. At Victoria, while the dawn tinted the majestic marble of the palatial Memorial with its imposing dome, we would hail a roving chai-wala and taste the sweet tea, tasting better for the burnt clay cups that it was swirled into from super-sized aluminium kettles. We finished the morning outing with a breakfast of *phuchka*[12] from a vendor before boarding a tram back, which had fans to cool the passengers as the day turned warmer, unlike buses (but one could go upstairs to feel the breeze on moving double-decker).

When we were about to leave for Britain, one of my aunts asked me what I would like to have before I left Kolkata. My answer was, a double-decker bus ride; and that is what we did, my aunt and I saw Kolkata from the front seat of the upper deck of a red double-decker bus,[13] boarding a number 10 at Ballygunge station and going to Haora, the twin town of Kolkata on the other side of the Hugli. Kolkata met Haora across the imposing cantilever Haora Bridge,[14] built between 1937 and 1943, a geometric marvel of silver steel, 99 metres high and running to 705 metres in length. And here in this west bank city of the Hugli is Haora Station, a spectacular red brick building designed by the British architect, Halsey Ricardo, opened in 1905, expanding on the second railway of India between Haora and the Bardhaman coalfields, begun in 1854. So Haora and Shealdah are the two main railway stations of the city, which is the headquarters of the Eastern and North-Eastern Railways of India, as Kolkata stands as the major city before India's rail and road arteries stretch to the troubled north east. Kolkata is also a home to the circular rail and local train network, which brings the floating population of the city in the daily influx of small traders, local producers, labourers and domestic help – the backbone of Kolkata's informal sector, without which the city would not pulsate as it does.

Kolkata was the city we aspired to come to, to study in as our parents and grandfathers had done. As I was growing up, I knew it had three universities, five medical and two engineering and technology colleges. There were the prestigious research institutes like the Bose Institute of Biological Sciences, the Saha Institute of Nuclear Physics, the Indian Statistical Institute, the Indian Institute of Management, the Marine Engineering College, to name some. As Kolkata students, we became a part of a vibrant network, organising and participating in inter-college and university fests and competitions, in spite of the dangerous tumult of Naxalite.[15] This was the city of the National Theatre, the Kolkata stage offering Bengali, Hindi and English plays for a veteran theatre-going public who had seen Sisir Bhaduri, Shambhu, Tripti and now Shaoli Mitra, and groups like Nandikar and Kallol bringing powerful drama and acting to the city, where Jatra, the folk theatre, also remains very much alive. I remember my feet sinking into the soft plush carpet of the Metro cinema and marvelling at the silver curtain rising at the Globe to show Julie Andrews dancing and singing 'The Hills are alive.' When the Rodin exhibition came to town, we queued up from six in the morning to get in and we were at the end of an already long row of art lovers. Kolkata hosts the Dover Lane Music Conference, the classical concert of India's leading maestros, which lasts through the night. People walk back early in the morning with the Bhairavi, the dawn raaga ringing in their ears. Kolkata was also the city of the British Council and the USIS (now called the American Center), with their libraries and seminars. The British Council introduced us to travelling theatre groups, visiting artists and scholars and was the nerve centre for Kolkata students.[16] This is what Kolkata has meant to many of us, a city of enthusiastic theatre, film, art, music, book and sports lovers. The city with which India's Nobel Laureates are associated, like Sir Ronald Ross, Rabindranath Tagore, Sir C.V. Raman, Mother Teresa and Amartya Sen, and the film director Satyajit Ray, who won a life-time's achievement Oscar for his work. But here is also a crowd that can agitate, gather near the Shahid Minar[17] to listen to fiery speeches or be sentimentally moved to play patriotic songs in the Maidan when faced by nine million fleeing a military pogrom in East Pakistan in 1971 and taking refuge in India, rousing Kolkata to dream for another nation's independence, in the birth of Bangladesh.

The Shahid Minar, the Victoria Memorial and the Haora Bridge have dominated the Kolkata skyline for a long time, and the latter's congestion remained a nightmare reality for people travelling between the two cities and for passengers hoping to catch trains at Haora. Finally the bridge has been matched by the second Hugli Bridge, a multicable toll bridge called the Vidyasagar Setu, built between 1978 and 1993, fanning out across 457 metres between Kolkata and Haora at the Rabindra Sadan end of the city.

In 1976 when the bridge was still a dream, another dream was realised very near where it was to be, in the first Kolkata Boi Mela, the Book Fair that was started by the Kolkata Publishers' and Booksellers Guild. It takes place at the Park Street end of the Maidan from the end of January till the first week of February. Originally a week, it now takes place over twelve days, and is visited by two million people, making its attendance the largest in the world. This is where I went to browse, buy books, see authors, watch artists and craftsmen at work, pick up reproductions of paintings by the famous artists of the Bengal School of Art and modern painters who graduated from the Kolkata Art College, scrutinise sketches and photographs of old Kolkata, marvel at the numerous magazines that mushroom in this city of readers and eat at the various food stalls, without which Kolkata would lose its appeal, as the love of good food goes with its love of books and art. In fact, the book district of Kolkata with its new and second-hand books and its publishing houses in College Street, symbolised by stalwarts like Dasgupta, is complemented by new world bookshops in Landmark and Crossword and specialised publishing firms like Seagull, showing that Kolkata still retains its hunger for books. And now it looks forward to the Book Mall, which will be the first of its kind, rivalling the shopping malls with car-parks that have changed the character of Kolkata.

But these commercial successes did not come in any easy arc of progressive development. The agitational politics of Kolkata, the trade unionism and the centre-left rift saw an erosion of Kolkata's industries. Companies which were associated with Bengal and Kolkata like Bengal Potteries, Bengal Lamp, Bengal Chemical, Calcutta Chemical, Sulekha (which vied with Quink ink), Dunlop,[18] Surfridge, Usha (which made fans and sewing machines), slowly became lost names across Bengal and India. It is true that companies like Bata and Hindustan Motors persevered. But many factories saw huge padlocks on their gates and industrial units took on a derelict, hopeless look. The industrial decline not only created job losses for workers but had a knock-on effect on the prospects of the middle class in Kolkata, which saw the emigration of young students to universities elsewhere and an upwardly mobile population seeking viable employment outside the state in India and abroad, especially in America. This trend has continued, leaving an ageing population living alone in big houses which were once built for two to three generations to live together.

The sense of loss and disillusion gripped the state as a land-reform movement that began in North Bengal near a small town called Naxalbari.It lit Kolkata in the late sixties and early seventies in a conflagration of Marxist-Leninist violence that wanted to shake the foundations of what it saw as a corrupt, decadent, dysfunctional bourgeois system that needed to be swept away by a revolution. In the coffee houses of Kolkata, nexus of many student revolutions, the storm in the coffee cup became a storm of actual confrontation between students and police. College Street – the street of bookshops, of Calcutta University's Ashutosh campus, Presidency and Sanskrit Colleges and Hindu School – was a battleground between the dreaming young, the disaffected populace and the establishment. The hit-lists which were drawn up by a section of the Naxalites, targeting people in key positions who were seen as enemies of the people, led to murders and counter-murders, turning the tide of public support against the Naxalites. The Naxalite movement[19] caught the city in a violence that made it dangerous for the young to stay in their homes for fear of arrest. The death of suspected Naxalites in police custody, the vanishing of those captured (both women and men), the settling of old scores by various factions under cover of the Naxalite movement, the relentless measures taken by the Indira Gandhi government to splinter the group from within with the help of the then state government, amounted to a good section of Kolkata's (and Bengal's) aspiring, intellectual youth being wiped out altogether.

So Kolkata, the city of adda, that untranslatable Bengali malady/obsession/culture/lifeline – call it what you will – that serious-light, intellectual conversation/discussion/debate about politics, cricket, football,[20] newspaper articles, theatre, film, war, anything... where young men[21] gather in tea stalls, in coffee houses, on the rowaks,[22] to solve the world's problems as it were, through adda, was suddenly transformed during the Naxalite days. Rowaks were uncannily empty and instead of young men commenting on and teasing passing girls, there was a city of young men in hiding. Yes, what was missing was the presence of carefree youngsters. We became alert to furtive footfall, running feet, someone knifed in broad daylight, sten gunshots ripping still afternoons and silent evenings, blood spilling over tramlines and those old French window shutters closing quickly over silent streets, afraid of being called on as witnesses.

It was not till the mid seventies that Kolkata was able to bounce back to its bustling activity and resume its claim to fame as 'the city of processions'. Agitational politics took on a different turn as a Marxist government came to power in 1977 to stay, perhaps forever... Processions continue, of workers, teachers, political parties, halting the slow traffic, knotting it in unimaginable convolutions in spite of measures to restrict times and roads for such spectacles, challenging the city's transport system. The challenges have been met with new flyovers arching across the city, blocking out familiar landmarks, and siphoning the ever-increasing car and bus traffic into new vehicular ducts.

The transport system of Kolkata has seen various challenges to its existing rivals. When I came back as a student to study in Kolkata, we witnessed the onslaught of the maroon minibuses, which came in with purpose built low roofs to discourage standing passengers and were a challenge to breathe in. Kolkatans, in their indomitable style, packed in like chickens in a wicker basket, the taller section folded once or twice in excruciating postures that would defeat medieval torture racks, till the minibus authorities had to revamp their buses to raise their ceilings, to let their passengers pile into every bit of space, squashed but upright. The minibuses remain, defying traffic rules in hair-raising races with each other and other buses, to scoop up passengers at bus-stops, the drivers and conductors hooting and urging themselves on, as if Kolkata is a sports ground for sprinting minibuses, totally oblivious of the lives they put at risk on the road and in their oven baking, claustrophobic, utterly choked interiors.

The state buses, battered and smashed with time, have seen many novel additions, such as limited-stop buses, 'specials' and deluxe buses, hiking fares that private buses have failed to compete with. Around the time I graduated from a student to an earning citizen, I was grateful for the upgraded rickshaw – the autorickshaw, painted yellow and black to match the Ambassador taxis and vying with their custom, offering single passenger rates as shuttle taxis on busy routes. As cycle rickshaws are banned from major sections of the metropolis, and hand pulled rickshaws are slow and laborious,[23] the autorickshaws offer seats that minibuses cannot assure and squeeze between spaces they cannot enter, giving hazardous rides at heart-stopping speed: passengers have to develop strong stomachs.

But amidst this cacophony of horns and beeps, came a new dream, overturning the alluvial underbelly of Kolkata, as hillocks appeared which soon grew grass and bushes, marring the Chowringhee's prestigious view, blotting the entire length of Kolkata in one long line from Tollygunge to Esplanade. This was the building of the metro, which became the definition of ultra chaos, till, miraculously, it was opened in 1984, running today from Tollygunge to

Dum Dum. For a long time, it was the only one in the country and remains the pride of the city.[24] This is where I would take my niece for a treat, no longer longing to see Kolkata from an ageing population of double-deckers or meandering trams, but happy to see the Kalighat pat paintings replicated, or colonial or sports scenes at various stations and walk out to the sound of Tagore songs played at Rabindra Sadan metro station, in an ambience that never fails to stimulate, baffle or astound, a subterranean world of cleanliness, order and meticulous clockwork precision.

All this has been possible because Kolkata has not seen the same kind of mob fury that has rocked the confidence of communities across India, especially in 1982[25] and 1992[26] It has remained relatively calm, since it had its fair share of communal violence in the pre-Partition days. So this city continues to celebrate its festivals with verve, Durga Puja[27] when families and visitors go round the city to admire the artistically sculptured images, the imaginatively structured *pandals*[28] and the amazing lights which are strung up to tell whole stories and contemporary events, or at Eid when around a hundred thousand Muslims pray at Park Circus Maidan and at Christmas when Park Street is strewn with lights and every grocery shop in the city sells fruit cakes.

Living in London in Barnes, in the early sixties, Christmas was the only festival I could link Kolkata with. Another similarity with Kolkata was the lack of parked cars then, which allowed us to play on the streets. One change that has come over the Kolkata middle class as it has elsewhere, albeit at a different pace, is the acquisition of cars. In the eighties when I returned to Barnes, I found cars parked in streets bereft of playing children. In Kolkata, only the rich had cars in the sixties and the most popular one remained the Ambassador for a long time. In the seventies and eighties, though private cars seemed to be in abundance on Kolkata streets, they were not owned by the general middle classes. With the liberalisation of the nineties, the banks started wooing customers with loans, changing the lifestyle of Kolkata's middle class, who now own cars, many of whose parents and grandparents didn't. And they live in flats bought again with bank and company loans, in apartment blocks where pigeons are not welcome, buildings which have replaced the old Kolkata houses of inner courtyards, continuous terraces, and house fronts with jhul barandas of ornate trellis work. In their place are multi-storeyed buildings with minimum balcony space and ground floors given over to car parks to accommodate the car population[29] of a crowded Kolkata, gated and with their own security systems.

Kolkata is ensnared by its tenancy laws, which make it impossible to evict old tenants paying absurdly low rent, fixed decades ago, and landlords lodging law suits have had grandchildren continuing the case, in the hope that great grandchildren might enjoy the by then degenerating family home. Another problem is the law of entailment, which makes it impossible sometimes to locate, identify and round up all joint owner/shareholders to restore or sell a property. So the beautiful but crumbling old houses, some with inner courtyards or trellis balconies, are handed over to 'promoters', who demolish them and build concrete blocks, raising the Kolkata skyline, where newspapers now have to be delivered by boys and men running up common stairs.

Kolkata is everyone's city, loathe to clear its pavements of pavement dwellers, its slums sitting side by side with gated multi-storeyed buildings, and refugees and economic migrants still drawn to its overburdened infrastructure. It is a city of contrasts with its millions of workers, its teeming middle class and entrepreneurial rich. Revolution has always fired the imagination of Kolkata and today a new revolution has brought hope to what Rajiv Gandhi once called the 'the dying city'. West Bengal's present Chief Minister, Buddhadev Bhattacharya, has welcomed the expansion of IT and a sector has come up for this purpose in the planned township area of Salt Lake. Many new institutes are added to reflect the city's changing interests and infrastructure like those offering courses in hotel management in a new world of global hospitality or others which rework old institutions in the West Bengal National University of Juridicial Sciences, necessary if one is to challenge not just the gothic dignity of Kolkata's High Court building, but its prolonged system of delayed justice, befitting only Dickens' Chancery. The challenge is to retain the grand old façade while instilling new methods to circumvent the colonial style red tapeism, to make way for rejuvenating economics, while not letting the poor be forgotten in the heady rush towards globalised success.

The very skies over Kolkata look different as the skyline has adjusted and altered to let its new brood of pigeons scour the horizon of a growing metropolis with a resurgent economy. Kolkata remains a home to a pan-Indian populace who have settled here, coming from the far west, like Rajasthan, the Punjab and Gujarat, from the deep south like Tamil Nadu, Andhra Pradesh and Kerala, from the neighbouring east like Orissa and Assam and Nepal in the north, joining the native West Bengali and east Bengali/East Pakistani/ Bangladeshi refugees and recent migrants in a city which may not be the economic or political capital, but prides itself on being the 'cultural capital of India'.

References and Bibliography

Bagchi, Jasodhara and Dasgupta, Subhoranjan. *The Trauma and the Triumph: Gender and Partition in Eastern India*. Kolkata: Stree, 2006.

Chaudhuri, Sukanta. *Calcutta: The Living City*. New Delhi: Oxford University Press, 1990, 1995, Vols I & II.

Chakrabarty, Prafulla K. *The Marginal Men*. Kolkata: Naya Udyog, 1999.

Das, Suranjan. *Communal Riots in Bengal, 1905–1947*. Delhi: Oxford University Press, 1993.

Fraser, Bashabi. *Bengal Partition Stories: An Unclosed Chapter*. London: Anthem Press, 2006.

Ray, Manas, 'Growing up Refugee', in *History Workshop Journal*, Issue 53, 2002, pp. 149–79.

Roy, Ranajit. *The Agony of West Bengal*. Kolkata: The New Age Publishers, second edition, 1972.

Samaddar, Ranabir. *Reflections on Partition in the East*. Kolkata: Vikas Publishing House Pvt. Ltd., 1999.

http://en.wikipedia.org/wiki/Kolkata

http://www.calcuttaweb.com/history.shtml

http://www.indiaseminar.com/2006/559/559%20belinda%%20wright.htm

Endnotes

1   The Bengali word for neighbourhood which has connotations of a community life and the sense of bonding it brings.

2   The newspaper in question is *The Statesman*, an English daily started in 1885 in Kolkata, which was estimated to have an approximate readership of 180,000 in a 2002 Indian Survey.

3   Literally, it means the kite's room, named after the ubiquitous bird of prey that lurked on the Kolkata horizon, watchful and looming.

4   I now wonder if that was his real name, for Noton is the name of a kind of white pigeon. Was it just a happy coincidence or a name affectionately given for a task he enjoyed, that stuck? I don't know.

5   Founded in 1784.

6   The library was moved in 1952 from Esplanade to Belvedere Building in Alipore.

7   Founded in 1875.

8   Founded in 1857.

9   This square could be a section of London on an unusually deserted day, without its typical Kolkata traffic or people.

10   Built in 1851 by the Scots indigo planter, Johnston, and reclaimed and made into the Tollygunge Club in 1895 by Sir William Cruickshank who was the Head of the Bank of Bengal.

11   Similar to the Meadows in Edinburgh.

12   Deep fried crispy balls filled with spiced potato and tamarind sauce.

13   Very much like a London bus.

14   Reminding one of the Forth Rail Bridge across the Firth of Forth.

15   Communist movement; also see note 19.

16   The Kolkata British Council is the first to have an Indian Director in Sujata Sen,

and is responsible for putting the process of twinning Kolkata with Edinburgh (the first UNESCO City of Literature) in motion.

17 Also known as the Ochterlony Monument.

18 Dunlop reopened on 31 October 2006.

19 It is interesting to note that the Naxalite Movement coincided with student revolutions elsewhere in the world. In the 1960s, American Universities saw a series of protests. There was the nationwide protest against the Vietnam War. In Latin America, this was the time of Ché Guevara and Fidel Castro's revolution, while in Paris, American and Latin American revolutionary protests inspired the Student Revolution of May 1968. In another context, China saw the beginning of the Cultural Revolution in 1966, which was to continue till 1978, around the time when Naxalites were finally released and free to become participating citizens of Indian social and economic life.

20 Kolkata is the home of India's leading football teams in Mohan Bagan (founded in 1889), Mohammedan Sporting (founded in 1891) and East Bengal (founded in 1920), which accounts for the city's passion for the game.

21 *Tha para* addas are usually dominated by young men, though the coffee houses, small restaurants and student canteens see a mixed crowd of young women and men.

22 The narrow platforms leading to houses.

23 They are now on the way out as they have disturbed the conscience of Kolkata for a long time.

24 Delhi too has a metro now which opened on 24 December 2002.

25 The attacks on Sikhs that followed Indira Gandhi's assassination by her Sikh bodyguards.

26 The repercussion of the demolition of the Babri Masjid (Mosque) at Ayodhya.

27 Durga Puja, the celebration of the coming of the Mother Goddess who kills the demon to make good win over evil, is an example of Bengal's inter-dependent economic and cultural fabric, when various artists and craftsmen from all castes and religions contribute. This community festival is part of their livelihood. This year, Durga was sculpted in the British Museum and immersed in the Thames.

28 Marquees that are erected to house the images and are built with artistic variations, mainly of bamboo and cloth, and can be made to look like the Taj Mahal or the British Museum, as suits the artist's fancy and the time.

29 The cars are now of multiple makes, both Indian and foreign.

The Theatres of Calcutta

Anjum Katyal

Let's start with a room. A room in an ageing house tucked away off a busy thoroughfare, a grand dame of a house from the days of the Raj, high ceilinged, marble floored, now beginning to show cracks and peeling plaster. The walls of the room are draped in black cloth from floor to ceiling, masking the various entrances. As I enter I am engulfed in dense, aromatic, herbal smoke, the kind we use against mosquitoes in traditional homes, a domestic ritual as the sun goes down. It serves a dual purpose here, keeps mosquitoes out and creates a tangible atmosphere that envelops you. Through the smoke I see, along the walls, bamboo and coir rope structures, like the scaffolding with which construction is undertaken in our city, but lashed together here to form the suggestion of pillared arcades holding up balconies and verandahs, a common architectural feature of the older part of the city. There is graffiti, there is a luridly violent film poster, some washing hung out to dry. This is a city street, then. Not one of the broad avenues down which buses thunder. A lane or bylane, with its mix of middle-class small shops and homes. A pure clean shaft of light slices through the smoke to focus on a tiny earthenware pot, cheap, our native equivalent of disposable ware, but friendlier to the earth. It is filled with a white powder. I climb the shaft of light with my eyes and it leads to a high beamed ceiling. I notice that there is a lighting grid in place. Wires looped and strung. I make my way to one end of the room, where mats on the floor await the audience. We are seated with our backs to a louvred French window, facing in to the room. Now I notice the lighting controls set up in a little alcove to my right; there is also someone with a computer controlling the sound that filters in. At the moment, it is music. Surprisingly eclectic: latin jazz, then be-bop, then something more Indian-sounding. Slowly the seating area fills. A handbell is rung twice. In the shadowy darkness beyond the intense shaft of light the figure of a young woman in white enters and lies down on a cheap string and bamboo cot, common poor man's furniture. The handbell rings again. The play begins.

Called *Intro: An Hour in the City*, this is a student production. In the sense that everyone involved with creating it is an undergraduate or finishing high school. It uses wit, humour, song and dance sequences, a live drummer and programmed music with sound effects, tableaus, leitmotifs, a larger-than-lifesize puppet-schoolboy who is outside the French window, at 'his' balcony, looking in, like us, on the streetlife that unfolds before us all. It is his seeing that we see. There is a girl giving birth in the shadows, alone in silent agony as two men fight, over and over, in a circularity of violence with no meaning and no end. There is a drunken garbage collector who, as he puts it, fights endlessly too, with the filth of the city. There are weary salesmen on foot, a newspaper vendor on a cycle and an 'intellectual' whose jargon-laden speech deteriorates into gibberish. There are street cries and voices offstage which intrude into the performance space, including the ubiquitous Kolkata protest procession, which disrupts life for the common man trying to complete daily chores. There is a car accident, a body dumped in the trash like so much more garbage. Textual references range from Shakespeare to current advertisement slogans to popular cinema. The spoken language moves between native Bengali and equally native English, in the unselfconscious manner of today's urban living. And the performance language is intensely theatrical and visual.

I start with this room because what it offers is in some ways a crystallised moment which holds several histories of the theatre of this city. As we move through this essay, these embedded histories will show. For one, it bespeaks other rooms that came before it. Rooms that housed the '*anganmancha*' theatre of Badal Sircar, for example. Badal Sircar is one of the most influential figures in the city's multi-faceted theatre scene. A playwright whose work since the sixties has shown the way to myriad directors of his texts, and to socially conscientised theatre workers who have sought to take a politicised theatre to the people. In the early 1970s, moving away from the proscenium stage for which he had written powerful, thought-provoking plays that made him one of the most often-produced playwrights on a national level, Badal

Sircar propounded his theory of a theatre that was free. Free in that it charged no entry, in that it was mobile, in that it did away with the technology and appurtenances of the proscenium and brought the focus back to the body and physicality of the actor, moving freely in space, and interacting directly with an audience seated up close and around him/her. This theatre was political, socially activist, it was premised on an honest human-to-human exchange, it was workshop-based and ensemble in style, as democratic as it was possible to be. He called it the Third Theatre, because in our context the First theatre was the urban Western- and colonial-influenced stage play; the Second Theatre was the folk or rural or semi-urban performance tradition which stretched back centuries and was usually mythological or historical in subject matter; and both were alive and flourishing simultaneously in and around the city. His was a third way. His group, Satabdi, performed in rooms with the audience sitting around and between the actors. The actors' bodies became different characters, inanimate objects, forces of nature. The plays dealt with concerns and issues of our times. There were songs, there was movement in silence, acrobatics. This was an intimate theatre, but they also evolved a performance style for the outdoors, for parks and public spaces, where hundreds of people sat or stood to watch, where they competed with traffic noises and other ambient sound, where the gestures were bigger and the physicality more pronounced. Badal Sircar's group still performs, and he, now in his eighties, is still active. There are scores of groups in and around the city (and the country) who trace their inspiration back to him. Street theatre groups, intimate theatre groups, nonverbal theatre groups, political activist theatre groups. His own inspiration came from the environmental theatre of Richard Shechner and from Grotowski amongst other international influences, filtered through a sensibility seeking a form of communication that was immediate, relevant, democratic and sincere.

International influences are woven into the very fabric of this city's theatre. After all, this was the capital of the Raj till 1911, and the cultural capital long before and after. It is emblematic that the very first stage play in Calcutta was produced by a Russian, Lebedeff, in Bengali. In 1795. From the late eighteenth century, there were theatre houses in Calcutta, modelled on theatres in London but clearly demarcated in terms of audience: there was theatre by the whites for the whites, imitative of whatever the London stage had to offer; and when the fast-growing Bengali bourgeoisie sought this form of entertainment, they produced and patronised their own. The proscenium stage with its invisible fourth wall was imported into the theatre of Calcutta and soon became the dominant mode of performance. Already existing in the local culture was an earlier performance form, the travelling theatre-in-the round, Jatra. This had a strong popular base, and fixed stylistic and structural features: the audience sat on three sides, the performers were visible even when not performing (entries and exits, for example, were often through the audience), it was performed in temporary spaces as it travelled through the countryside, it incorporated certain set characters like the *sutradhara* (the narrator, or stage manager, as he is sometimes designated) and the *bibek* (literally, conscience), it was loose in structure, incorporating songs, live music, bits of crude comic by-play and continuing all night long, the themes were usually mythological and epical. Jatra was to have a major influence on the evolving hybrid theatre that the Bengali bourgeois babu developed in Calcutta. Jatra even now is a popular presence, particularly in the environs of the city.

English and Bengali became the two major language streams in which Calcutta theatre was done. Even today, the two theatre worlds are seen as divided. They perform in different auditoriums, they call to different audiences, circulate through different performance circuits. This division goes back to the very beginning of urban theatre in the city. Another history *Intro* incidentally comments on: by choosing a neutral performance space not identified in the popular perception with one or the other, by incorporating both languages in the most natural way. By signalling that the youth are ready to move beyond these language divisions into a new theatre of the city.

As the urban theatre grew and established itself through the nineteenth century, it became a space of subversion, protest and challenge to the status quo. Orthodox caste restrictions on intermingling were broken here; contact between all sections of society and religious groups was promoted; women (initially socially outcast singer-dancer courtesans) were introduced onto the stage in the teeth of a raging debate on how this was promoting public immorality. Innumerable plays enacted a criticism of traditional customs and values designated backward and regressive as society rapidly grew increasingly urban and egalitarian in some respects. And as nationalist awareness grew, the Raj was increasingly criticised. *Neel Darpan* (*Indigo Mirror*, 1872) is a landmark play that castigated the callous indigo planters for the plight of the peasants on their plantations. It set off a storm of protest and sired a string of plays on similar themes. So much so that the British authorities decided to slam down a Dramatic Performances Act (1876), through which they tried to monitor seditious productions. The Act is still in place in Calcutta, although on paper only. Theatre's response was to use allegory instead of direct political critique, and suddenly there was a plethora of plays set in ancient and medieval times which talked of tyranny and oppression to an audience which perfectly understood the subtext.

This skein of social and political critique is perhaps the single strongest feature of theatre in the city (as even *Intro* demonstrates in its direct accusation that we the well-off live in a city we no longer care to see). In the 1940s, it flowered into the Indian People's Theatre Association (IPTA), arguably the single biggest cultural force in the shaping of performance culture in independent India. This movement consisted of the leading creative minds of the time – singers, actors, playwrights, musicians, composers, dancers – who gathered under its umbrella of broadly left ideology to promote performance art with social empowerment as its goal. As the initial power and coherence of the movement began to crumble in the succeeding decades, many of the stalwarts once associated with it left to start groups of their own, or inspired successors to do so. As a result, one of Calcutta's most typical theatre formations, the 'group theatre' came into being. This was a movement in its own right, of amateur (or perhaps more accurately, volunteer) groups comprised of committed theatre practitioners who hold day jobs which allow them to support their regular theatre activity. Typically, they will have one director-actor around whom the group has crystallised, and a cluster of men and women group members who form the ensemble. There are set venues, mostly government theatres with lower charges, in which these groups perform. They move from one production to the next, usually selecting plays which offer some sort of social comment. Art for art's sake is not an indulgence commonly encountered here.

However, one outstanding figure, Utpal Dutt, did succeed in taking political theatre to the level of high art in the sixties. Marxist playwright, director and actor, Dutt's memorable productions still remain benchmarks in the theatre-going memory. His proscenium productions were a virtuoso combination of excellent production values (particularly sets, sound and light), tight ensemble acting (by his Little Theatre Group), and high melodrama. His *Kallol* (*Waves*, 1965) on the Royal Indian Navy Mutiny of 1946, considered one of the decisive moments that led to the British deciding to give up India, is still talked about for its light effects and dramatic staging. Later he took an active interest in the rejuvenation of the Jatra form as well.

Group theatre is still ubiquitous in the city. Today, it is Bengali and Hindi proscenium theatre on a shoe string budget; it has a regular (albeit dwindling, not to mention ageing) middle class audience. Nandikar, Chetana, Anya Theatre, are amongst the oldest and most active of these groups. Interestingly, there is now a younger generation, emerging from within the group, which has taken over the leadership and is carrying the theatre forward. One sees more experimentation in these cases, with venue, subject matter and performance style. A sign of vitality and life.

In this discussion of the many theatres of Calcutta I have stayed with theatre that is practitioner-driven as opposed to corporate sponsorship-driven. This is not to say that the theatre I have talked of spurns sponsorship; rather that it exists in spite of and without such sponsorship if necessary. There is a layer of theatre activity in the city that consists of plays mounted by large corporates for invited guests, performed in elite auditoriums or hotels and often imbibed over supper or cocktails. This is part of a trend that is growing all over the world; as such it cannot be claimed as distinctively Calcuttan in any way, apart from the occasional accident of venue. The group theatre described above often accepts such 'call shows', which pay well enough to cover a couple of regular performances; but they are not their *raison d'etre*.

If I have been able to convey something of the complexity, the layering, the multiplicity and the historical provenance of the many theatres of Calcutta, I have done what I set out to do. That room we walked into at the beginning of this essay was a microcosm of theatre in the city. It held the past, the several presents, and the future. And if *Intro* is anything to go by, the future looks bright.

Bengali Cinema

Sangeeta Datta

To write an overview of Bengali cinema seems a daunting task as this industry, since the turn of the twentieth century, has made a significant contribution to Indian cinema. It is imperative to be selective and I have chosen to examine the period from 1970 to the present day, with a focus on significant filmmakers who worked alongside or after Satyajit Ray. Some of Ray's contemporaries, like Mrinal Sen and Tapan Sinha, are still sporadically active in the industry, while younger directors have carved their own niche and continue to win global attention with their work. Any film critic or practitioner of world cinema will know that Bengal and Kerala are the spawning grounds of independent cinema in India. The Bengali film industry has been nicknamed Tollywood, from the Tollygunge studios in south Calcutta.

Ten years after Indian independence, Satyajit Ray showcased Bengali film to a global audience. Influenced by European and Russian cinema and steeped strongly in his own culture, Ray created the groundbreaking *Apu* trilogy. Ray's films marked a formal breaking away from melodrama and theatricality and offered a modern idiom in Bengali cinema. In 1967, the Naxalbari peasant movement sparked a major student agitation in Calcutta. There followed a decade of political upheaval and armed movements by party cadres and urban students – a result of the split between the right and the militant left wing of the Communist Party of India. The turbulent politics of the seventies was captured both in Ray's films and in the films of Mrinal Sen. Having gained global recognition in the sixties for period films like *Charulata* and *Jalsaghar*, as well as the Apu trilogy, Ray made a major shift to contemporary Calcutta for his seventies trilogy – *Pratidwandi, Seemabaddha* and *Jana Aranya*.

Based on Sunil Gangopadhyay's novel, *Pratidwandi* (*The Adversary*, 1970) coincided with the first film in Mrinal Sen's own Calcutta trilogy. The protagonist, Siddhartha (Dhritiman Chatterjee), fails to get a job despite endless waiting in stifling interview rooms. Faced with the life choices of his younger, rebel brother – a Naxalite – and his sister's affair with her employer, he becomes disillusioned and eventually leaves Calcutta. The city's political fabric is revealed in a big political rally in the Maidan, while a strong nostalgia is evoked for an irretrievable past.

The second film in Ray's Calcutta trilogy, *Seemabaddha* (*Company Limited*, 1971), addresses corporate corruption. The protagonist, Shyamalendu Chatterjee (Barun Chanda) – a sales manager – enters into a dishonest deal with his factory's personnel manager, through which he obtains a promotion. The political apathy of the newly rich urban class is given a critical examination. Loss of innocence, and the alienation caused by political upheaval and the growth of capitalism are the concerns underpinning Ray's city films.

Jana Aranya (*The Middleman*, 1975) marks the final part of Ray's trilogy and has been termed 'his most disaffected melodrama'. Furthering the themes of corruption and unemployment, the protagonist Somenath (Pradip Mukherjee) fails his university exams due to unfair assessment. Roaming the streets in search of a job, Somenath is befriended by a trader who teaches him to work as a middleman – a buyer and seller. He eventually has to procure a prostitute for a mill owner and, after a trip through nocturnal Calcutta, he ends up selling his friend's sister. Possibly the darkest of Ray's urban films, the world on show here (contextualised by the Emergency situation) is devoid of hope and light.

Meanwhile, Ritwik Ghatak's last film, *Jukti, Takko Aar Gappo* (*Reason, Debate and a Story*, 1974), reflects the anxieties of the time. In the journey mould, Ghatak casts himself as the drunken intellectual Neelkantha, drifting through Bengali landscapes. On his way he is joined by fellow travellers including a Bangladeshi refugee girl, a Sanskrit teacher, a noted writer, a trade union leader and a Chou mask artist. He argues and debates politics with a group of Naxalite students and is finally killed in a police ambush. Made in his last days, Ghatak's illness and alcoholism lend a surreal drift to the film. The lost world of nature is represented by Chou dance and Baul song, while the encounter with the Naxalites and the theme of writer-turned-pornographer stand as harsh critiques of contemporary urban politics.

Mrinal Sen witnessed the partition of Bengal after independence from British rule. Associated with the Indian People's Theatre Association (IPTA) and active in leftist politics, he drew on several influences in his work (Truffault, Fellini, Bresson, Solano, Getino). His *Bhuvan Shome* signalled the New Cinema movement, which worked towards producing low-budget alternative cinema.

The first of his Calcutta trilogy, *Interview* (1970), offers a Brechtian look at residual colonial attitudes in middle class Bengal. The second, *Calcutta 71* (1971), uses several short stories by Bengali authors and dramatists to 'define history and put poverty in its right perspective'. The narratives offer microscopic insights into the lives of refugees and slum dwellers, the legal system of the seventies, and the Bengal famine of the forties. The film's screenings became rallying points for student activists, with discussions on revolutionary cultural aesthetics, and were often under police surveillance.

Padatik (*The Guerilla Fighter*, 1973) – third in the trilogy – extends the powerful political language of its predecessors. An urban political party worker (Dhritiman Chatterjee) escapes police custody and finds refuge in the apartment of an upper class woman. He reflects on the split of the Communist Party and finds time to take stock of the politics in his home state of Bengal.

A critique of urban middle class family values was powerfully extended in Sen's *Ek Din Pratidin* (*And Quiet Flows the Dawn*, 1979), in which a young girl (Mamata Shankar), the sole bread winner in a family of seven, does not return home after work. Through the night of waiting every family member realises how dependent they are on Chinu and the drama reveals their insecurities and selfish motives. The setting – cramped tenements and the big indifferent city beyond – underlines the anonymity of the urban worker, both in society and within their own family structure. This was the first of Sen's more introspective dramas, and enquired into the real place for women in the changing social mileu as well as in the workplace.

Two other prolific and influential directors in Bengal, Tarun Majumdar and Tapan Sinha, continued the literary reformist style of filmmaking, with middle budget productions catering to a growing Bengali middle class. They carried on the tradition of socials (family stories) based on classic novels, transferring the respectability of literature to cinema. They are the last commercial Bengali directors to trace ancestry to Devaki Bose, P.C. Baruah and Bimal Roy, and the style of fifties art house cinema.

Tapan Sinha started at New Theatres with Nitin Bose and Bimal Roy. He spent some time in Pinewood Studios around 1950. His best known works have their basis in literature – Tagore's *Atithi* (*The Guest*, 1965), *Kshudita Pashan* (*Hungry Stones*, 1960) and *Kabuliwala* (1956); Samaresh Bose's *Nirjan Saikatey*; and Shankar's *Ek Je Chilo Desh* (1970). His *Apanjan* (1968) was one of the early responses to the rise of the Naxalite movement among urban Bengali youth. His political awareness and social critique found powerful expression in women's issues such as the legal stand on rape cases, as in *Adalat O Ekti Meye* (*Courtroom and a Girl*, 1981). Turning his attention to physical disability, Sinha directed Soumitra Chatterjee in a national award winning film, *Wheelchair* (1994), which he also wrote.

Tarun Majumdar's *Palatak* (1963; later made in Hindi as *Rahgir*) featured popular songs by Hemanta Mukherjee and was highly successful. But Majumdar is best known for his romantic musical *Balika Bodhu* (1967), a lyrical teen love story set against a rural backdrop. Through the seventies Majumdar made popular films like *Nimantran* (1971) and *Phuleshwari* (1974). The conflict of the city-country divide was freshly presented to the eighties audience with the very popular hit *Dadar Kirti* (1980). His are social message films with the populist trappings of romance and good music. They catered to a large middle class viewership which enjoyed the comfort zone of literary cinema. Continuing his interest in women's stories, Majumdar offered another hit film in 2002 – a rural lyrical story, *Aalo* – part produced by the lead actress, Rituparna Sengupta.

The Bengali film industry faced a crisis and hit a new low in production figures in the late seventies. The problems were manifold. Shortage of proper release chains, the black-money racket, the distributor-exhibitor stranglehold on producers, the monopoly of theatres, lack of modern studio and lab facilities, poor technical equipment and a paralysing artistic crisis. The number of theatre outlets remained static, studios were closing down and there was no fresh investment in the industry. The mainstream industry was unable to find a successor to the legendary star pair of Uttam Kumar and Suchitra Sen, who led the golden era of Tollygunge films. Mithun Chakravorty delivered hits as a Stallone-like action hero in B-grade movies, while Prasenjit Chatterjee has ruled commercial films for the last twenty years but never reached the iconic status enjoyed by Kumar.

The video market and rampant film piracy further shrunk the sparse intakes. Much of the home talent migrated to Bombay. Films with hackneyed plots and poor actors, mechanical imitations of Bombay films by mediocre directors, catered to semi-literate viewers. Tollygunge was gasping for breath. Urban middle class viewers who had inherited a taste for literary drama and high aesthetics now had only a handful of filmmakers catering to their tastes, and these were struggling for funds.

By the early eighties a surge of new talent was evident in Bengal. The new filmmakers, nurtured by the New Cinema movement, began with a command over their medium and a belief in the social relevance of cinema. The government played a constructive role, providing small subsidies and infrastructural facilities for film production. Nandan, the art film centre, was set up in 1985, intended as a focal point for disseminating film culture. Today it is common to see filmmakers and critics watching and discussing cinema there. In 1987 Rupayan, the first colour laboratory in the eastern zone, became operational. Institutionalised recognition, in the form of national awards, premiere telecast on national television, the Panorama section of the Indian film festival (showcasing the best Indian films) and increased access to international festivals, yielded a new culture for new cinema: a culture which bred some of the best Bengali directors.

I have chosen to restrict my discussion to the four most influential filmmakers after Satyajit Ray. These are Buddhadev Dasgupta, Goutam Ghosh, Aparna Sen and Rituparno Ghosh. During the eighties, Ray made his satirical *Hirak Rajar Deshey* (1981), the telefilms *Pikoo* and *Sadgati*, and a much hyped adaptation of Tagore's *Gharey Bairey* (*The Home and the World*, 1984). His last trilogy, comprising *Ganshatru* (*Enemy of the People*, 1989), *Shakha Proshakha* (*Branches of the Tree*, 1990) and *Agantuk* (*Stranger*, 1991), was concerned with corruption and moral responsibility and was essentially about human loneliness.

Some eighties filmmakers explored the cultural aftermath of Naxalism and the political turbulence of the previous decade. Dasgupta's generation witnessed the crushing of the Naxal movement, the making of Bangladesh, and Indira Gandhi's declaration of Emergency. Already a published poet, Dasgupta quit his job as a lecturer at Calcutta University and started training himself as a filmmaker, creating short films and documentaries. By the time he started on his first feature film he already had hands-on experience of editing, camera and sound recording. Beginning with a small grant from the West Bengal government, he had to rely on funds from friends to complete this film. *Duratwa* (1978), which eventually formed a triptych with *Grihayuddha* (1982) and *Andhi Gali* (1984), examines the contemporary social and political situation from the viewpoint of the guilt-ridden middle class. Concern for the poor and dispossessed lay behind *Neem Annapurna* (1979). Dasgupta drew on modern literature for many of his films, adapting stories by Sirshendu Mukhopadhyay, Kamalkumar Majumdat and Dibyendu Palit, and revisited the 'tiger man' of his childhood in *Bagh Bahadur* (*Tiger Man*, 1989). The villager who masquerades as a tiger in the countryside is an effective symbol of a traditional way of life that is being lost in an increasingly commercial world.

One of Dasgupta's significant films is *Tahader Katha* (*Their Story*, 1992), in which Shibnath (an award winning Mithun Chakravorty), a former freedom fighter, becomes disillusioned after independence. The country is divided, Bengal split into halves. Shibnath returns from prison and the mental asylum to find things have changed, and that he is a misfit in his new surroundings. All attempts to rehabilitate him fail, and he is left adrift and lost in this divided land, just as his ideals are.

Following his city films, Dasgupta returns repeatedly to the rural lands of Purulia and Birbhum and places human drama within natural settings. In fact nature plays an active part in the narratives, and characters live with the elements – wide skies over flat land, green woods, rivers and sometimes the sea.

Charachar (*The Shelter of Wings*, 1993) centres around the bird catcher Lakhinder who ironically likes to set his birds free. Lakhinder loves the trees and the birds who live in them. They are signs of freedom for his poetic soul. He loses his wife to another man, is unable to commit to another girl who loves him, and destroys his career. But as he loses his grip on material life, the birds provide a metaphor for his soaring spirit. The sustained beauty of the visual image and the layers of music give the film a dream like quality, close to poetry.

Dasgupta has been prolific over the last few years, working on low budget films and successfully obtaining European funding for his projects, most of which are about rural worlds remote from city life. He returns very often now to the familiar flat land of his childhood, the unique topography and light enabling the fablesque nature of his primal tales of man and nature. *Uttara* (*The Wrestlers*, 2001) examines male sexuality through the story of two friends who work at a remote railway station where life seems to stand still. When one marries a beautiful village girl, their friendship gradually sours. Jealousy and suspicion mar their primal, innocent world. Eventually the wrestlers take to the floor in semi darkness, in what could be a fight to death.

Mondo Meyer Upakhyan (*Tales of a Naughty Girl*, 2003) examines the relationships between the women in a whorehouse in a rural district of Calcutta. Strongly reminiscent of Shyam Benegal's *Mandi*, this film casts Rituparna Sengupta as an ageing sex worker.

Dasgupta's most recent film, *Kalpurush* (2006), addresses the father-son relationship (Mithun Chakraborty and Rahul Bose). In a fantasy or dream-like reverie, the son asks his father questions never asked in real life. Through subtle psychological drama and sensitive examination of relationships and human nature, and through poetic images that linger and haunt our dreams, Dasgupta's films display a self assurance and mastery. He shares the understated style which he so strongly admired in Ray, and above all he shows a deep humanity.

Goutam Ghosh was active in student politics in sixties Calcutta. He started as a journalist and fringe theatre director, and his photojournalism and early documentaries were strongly influenced by documentary filmmaker Sukhdev. Since his early films, Ghosh has done his own camerawork, screenplay, music and editing. His first film, *Mabhoomi* (*Motherland*, 1979), was based on the Telengana peasant uprising in 1949. Since then he has dealt with marginalised characters and extreme poverty – *Paar* (*River Crossing*, 1984) and *Antarjali Yatra* (*The Last Journey*, 1987), two of his best films – and made one of the more important Indo-Bangladesh collaborative projects, *Padma Nadir Majhi* (*Boatman of River Padma*, 1992). In Ghosh's words: 'I have shown human struggle in the face of poverty and oppression and natural elements – but have searched for the victorious human spirit which triumphs at the end.'

More recently, Ghosh has been drawn to the city and the death of ideals in a rapidly changing market. In *Dekha* (2002), he directs Soumitra Chatterjee as the blind poet who struggles with writer's block. The figure of the writer trying to match his imaginary world with the consumer driven market around him reappears again in his latest film, *Yatra* (*Journey*, 2006), a semi autobiographical narrative about a writer's journey and his romantic vision of the past. The image of the lost woman in the rain or mist recurs in his films, symbolic of a lost and irretrievable past.

The most talked about of Ghosh's recent films has been *Abar Aranya* (*In the Forest Again*, 2003), an imaginative sequel to Ray's *Days and Nights in the Forest* (1970) and for which he secured the original cast. The three friends of the earlier film (Soumitra Chatterjee, Suvendhu Chatterjee, Samit Bhanja; the fourth, Robi Ghosh, is dead) take their families back to the forest. No longer young and carefree, they carry new pressures and concerns with them. It's not just local politics but global events taking their toll. A young girl in the group is traumatised by 9/11, in which she lost her boyfriend. Ghosh flags up concerns about generational conflicts, changing moral values and new forms of displacement – echoed in the works of Dasgupta (*Kalpurush*), Aparna Sen (*Mr and Mrs Iyer*) and Rituparno Ghosh (*Ashukh*).

A Satyajit Ray discovery (in *Teen Kanya*, 1961), Aparna Sen worked for several years as the lead actress in Calcutta, till she grew tired of playing stereotypes and non-challenging roles and decided to become a director herself. Daughter of the eminent film critic Chidannda Dasgupta, she was exposed to European films at the film society set up by Ray and her father. Her first film, *36 Chowringhee Lane* (1981), produced by Shashi Kapoor, turned away from the political concerns of the State and offered a microcosmic view of the marginal Anglo-Indian community in Calcutta. Jennifer Kapoor (nee Kendal), wife of Shashi, played the lead part of a lonely school teacher in Calcutta. Sen displayed great control over her medium, modelling her work on European art house, and sparked a series of women-centric productions.

Made at the time of the women's movement in India, *Parama* (1985) caused national controversy with its theme of a middle class housewife (Raakhee Gulzar) who has an extramarital affair with an expatriate photographer (Mukul Sharma). After an attempted suicide, Parama rediscovers her own identity, stripped of the social role that she played in the conventional family structure. The film offered a message of liberation from gender roles and became a pivotal discussion point for students, like myself, in Calcutta.

Sati (1989) explored the oppression of women and the tyranny of superstitions in rural Bengal and featured Shabana Azmi. *Yuganta* (1995) continued grappling with marital relationships at a time when Sen was very depressed with political and environmental issues, including the Gulf War. *Yuganta* also explores the mythical idea of the four eras and an apocalyptical end. Critics note this as Sen's first breaking out from Satyajit Ray's school of filmmaking.

Sen came back with powerful and influential films in the English language. With *Mr and Mrs Iyer* (2001), Sen moves out of the Bengali domestic space to take a panoramic view of the nation in communal strife in the wake of the Hindu-Muslim riots and to reflect on the ways in which larger issues impinge on interpersonal relationships. A cross section of Indians travel in a bus through picturesque North Bengal. A young Tamil girl (Sen's daughter, Konkona) protects her Muslim companion (Rahul Bose) by claiming he is her husband. In the following days a tender relationship grows between the two, as they are locked in a guest house together while riots paralyse the town. Sen raises questions of citizenship and nationhood in this profound and humanitarian drama. Her friend and colleague, Goutam Ghosh, was director of photography.

In 2005, Sen deployed an extraordinarily powerful cast to make *15 Park Avenue* – a drama set among a non-Bengali family in Calcutta. A college professor (Shabana Azmi) has to deal with her schizophrenic sister (Konkona Sen Sharma) and ageing mother (Waheeda Rehman). Sen's most poignant script yet, this film deals with mental health issues in a realistic manner but more importantly it reveals the deftly changing, mercurial relationships in a family structure. Both this and *Mr and Mrs Iyer* have won Presidential Awards, as well as global accolades. Sen shows profound empathy with the human predicament – an essential humanist.

Working within the realist school of Satyajit Ray and Aparna Sen, the younger filmmaker Rituparno Ghosh has probably been the most prolific auteur. Quitting his job in an advertising firm, he made a children's film then cast Aparna Sen in his first feature, *Uneeshey April* (*19th April*, 1994). Inspired by Autumn Sonata, it deals with the difficult relationship between a mother (Sen, an established dancer) and her emotionally disturbed daughter (Debasree Roy, in a National Award winning performance). Much feted by the local media (Ghosh was an editor of a film magazine and hosted television shows), since then his women-oriented films have been eagerly awaited and highly acclaimed.

Dahan (*Crossfire*, 1997) scathingly attacks middle class notions about women's respectability and honour. It is based on Suchitra Bhattacharya's story, drawn in turn from a real life incident, in which a young woman is molested on the streets by a group of urchins. A young female journalist intervenes and reports the case to the police. But the victim's marital family do not allow her to appear in court as it would mean loss of face for them. The young bride finally leaves the claustrophobic home. Blending journalistic realism with a lyrical epistolary style, Ghosh exposes the patriarchal structures of conventional families and elicits memorable performances from his actors.

Ghosh displays fine attention to detail and great command over form in *Bariwali* (*Mistress of the House*, 1999), another woman-centric slice-of-life story in which a middle aged spinster's routine existence is disturbed when a film unit arrives to shoot in her house. (The process of film production also becomes part of the narrative in the Agatha Christie inspired *Shubho Muhurat* (2003) and the recently concluded *Khela* (*The Chase*, 2006).

If *Dahan* evoked Sen's *Parama*, then *Utsav* (2000) was an inspired extension to Ray's *Shakha Prosakha* (1990). Against the background of Durga Puja and festivity, the members of a large family meet in an old house outside Calcutta where the aged matriarch (Madhavi Mukherjee) lives. Every sibling has some secret to hide and tensions are high as the ancestral home is put up for sale. But all is resolved as the festival ends and the younger sister moves in to live with her mother. Ghosh's fascination with old architecture and traditional festivals is blended here with an intricate soundscape of the city. From *Utsav* began Ghosh's long association with a core team – cinematographer Abheek Mukherjee, set designer Indranil Ghosh, editor Arghyakamal Mitra. This was also one of the earliest Bengali films to have a non-resident Indian invest money as producer.

Ghosh moved to a much larger canvas with his adaptation of Tagore's *Chokher Bali* (2003) – a period drama set around 1902. Setting aside his local repertoire, he cast Bollywood glamour queen and erstwhile Miss Universe Aishwarya Rai in the title role of Binodini – a widow living in an upper class household in Calcutta. The young man of the house falls for her and they begin a passionate affair. Once again Ghosh questions the social role of conformity assigned to a widow. Produced on a larger budget than any Bengali film and strung on a wider landscape, the drama spans Calcutta and Benaras and ends with the partition of Bengal. It was dubbed for a Hindi version and had a successful national run, as well as being shown overseas.

The publicity resulting from *Chokher Bali* catapulted Ghosh into the front ranks of the Indian film industry. With Bombay actors Aishwarya Rai and Ajay Devgan, Ghosh made the Hindi film *Raincoat* (2004) – an interior drama about old lovers meeting on a rainy afternoon. Inspired by 'The Gift of the Magi', this small scale drama elicited Aishwarya's best performance to date.

In 2005, Ghosh turned to another well known story to make another period drama, entitled *Antarmahal* (*Views of the Inner Chamber*). This marked the launch of his own production house and a tie in with Amitabh Bacchan's company, AB Corps. Antarmahal introduced Sharmila Tagore's daughter Soha Ali Khan and Bombay stars Abhishek Bacchan and Jackie Shroff. During the British Raj, a wealthy landlord obsessed with producing an heir marries a second wife. The young bride, imprisoned in the mansion, is sexually abused every night. She falls in love with the sculptor who comes to create an image of a goddess. This has frightening consequences for both the women (Rupa Ganguly, Soha Ali Khan) in the household. A disturbing psychological drama, beautifully shot and designed, the film caused controversy in Bengal, sparking a debate about its sex scenes. The Bengali audience, who had loved Ghosh throughout his work, turned on him when he pushed them beyond their comfort zone.

Antarmahal is perhaps the darkest of Ghosh's films. He has displayed a remarkable control over diverse genres of filmmaking. With *Dosar* (*Companion*, 2006), Ghosh is reminiscent of Almadovar, scathingly stripping gender relations in an urban context. His constant examination of the female psyche and female identity and the magical way in which he has cast older Bengali actresses (Aparna Sen, Raakhee, Sharmila Tagore, Jaya Bacchan, Madhavi Mukherjee) brings to mind *All About my Mother* and the recent *Volver*.

Currently in production with the black comedy *Sunglass*, Ghosh returns to his obsessive concern – scrutinising marital relations and examining power politics in the gender debate. A gay activist, he talks of his empathy and innate understanding of the female mind, preferring to call his films 'middle class cinema', as he is nurtured by middle class sensibilities. His minute dissection of family and social relationships has led critics to compare him to Satyajit Ray.

Bengali cinema faces a future of possibilities and paradoxes. Commercial cinema has had a good year, with a couple of box office successes. The recent success of Sandip Ray's adaptation of his father's (Satyajit's) sleuth story underscores the need for literary family films. Today, commercial producers are travelling to Bangkok, Singapore and even London to shoot their film sequences. The highly imitative candy floss romance and wedding themes prove very popular in small towns and semi-rural districts. The literate middle class audience enjoys the art house films of some of the best filmmakers in the country. There are more theatres now in the city of Calcutta, including a large number of multiplexes in which art house films can be shown. Digital technology offers the possibility of making small budget films for the Metro audience. Nandan – the state sponsored film theatre – remains a vibrant hub for film festivals and screenings. Indeed, the film society culture introduced by Satyajit Ray in 1947 continues to sustain an audience which believes in cinema as an art form and enjoys exposure to films from abroad. The film culture – including festivals, publications, talks and seminars – is as integral a part of the city spirit as street theatre and fringe drama.

The Tollygunge studios in the extreme south end of Calcutta churn out about twenty films a year; for regular sustenance, most studios have one or more floors dedicated to television soaps. Most art house directors alternate between telefilms and features, indicating the changing mediascape of the city. Industry costs for labour and equipment are among the lowest in the country and this often leads to trade union problems and industry strikes. Low costs also attract television soaps, Bombay productions like Pradeep Sarkar's *Parineeta* (2005) and international projects such as Florian Gallagher's *Shadows of Time* (2005). A middle budget feature film (150 minutes) can still be made under one crore rupees (£120,000, approximately), whereas an A-grade Bollywood film can cost over thirty crores. In the face of Bombay film entertainment and Bollywood imitatives ruling the Bengali commercial circuit, box office recovery is uncertain. Thus small budget, controlled productions facilitate quick production and release. For instance in South Calcutta, one theatre – Priya Cinema – caters entirely to a middle class literate audience and most art house films have their first run there.

As the consumer market grows, certain changes are evident. Corporate houses in Calcutta and Bombay are developing a slate of films with several Bengali filmmakers. Others, like Goutam Ghosh and Rituparno Ghosh, are foraying into Bombay with higher budget projects.

Most importantly, there is a growing expatriate Bengali audience all over the world – chiefly the professional generation in North America and two generations of migrants in Europe and the UK. The demand for good art house films is met by DVD markets and often by pirated tapes. Whenever I have organised screenings and retrospectives in London, the films have played to full houses, with the viewers asking for more. With a systematic distribution in place, the art house films can get marketed. Unfortunately, in the West, Bollywood appropriates all commercial space for Indian cinema. This hegemony must be broken as the audience tires of pastiche and kitsch.

As with the struggle of the independent American filmmaker against Hollywood, Bengali filmmakers and producers must find means of selling and showing their films. Film festivals like London, Berlin, Venice, Toronto, Chicago and LA showcase films from Bengal every year. Buddhadev Dasgupta, Rituparno Ghosh and Goutam Ghosh have toured extensively promoting their films and have broken some ground. Small investments in Bengali films by wealthy expatriates are a recent indicator of collaboration in future, and hopefully of new markets and a growing audience.

References

Ashish Rajadhyaksha and Paul Willemen ed. *Encylopaedia of Indian Cinema,* BFI/ Oxford University Press, 1994.
Seven Decades of Bengali Cinema, Nandan, West Bengal Film Centre, 1990.
Kiranmoy Raha, *Bengali Cinema,* Nandan, West Bengal Film Centre, 1991.
Chidananda Dasgupta, *Talking about Films,* Orient Longman, 1981.
Andrew Robinson, *Satyajit Ray: The Inner Eye,* Rupa Publications, 1990.
Author's interviews with Buddhadev Dasgupta, Goutam Ghosh, Aparna Sen and Rituparno Ghosh, 2004–06.
Sangeeta Datta, *The Way I See It* (documentary on Indian women filmmakers), 2000.

A Celtic Chakra

Kenny Munro

As a visual artist, my philosophy of empowerment via the arts has recently been expressed in a series of collaborations between Scots and Bengali artists. This experience has strengthened my belief that the arts in Scotland should be brought centre stage – as in India, where the arts are anchored within the spirit of community.

Kolkata's links to Scotland are immediately palpable – jute mills, canals, some very familiar church architecture, even an area called Fort William. In the Scottish Cemetery, remarkable Celtic and Moghal style head-stones stand side by side – like a Piranesi composition. In my practise, I am inspired by the vision of Sir Patrick Geddes, Scottish ecologist and town planner, who worked in India between 1914 and 1924 – the connection which drew me to Bengal in the first place.

School of Art and Craft, Kolkata

Tandra Chanda and Pulak Ghosh run a small School of Art and Craft in Asgar Mistri Lane, Kolkata. Tandra specialises in stained glass, creating her 'painted glass panels' through an exacting process, first making a clear outline of the composition on the reverse side of the glass, then overlaying successive layers of colour. Her husband, Pulak, is a painter who sets unexpected 'creatures' and symbols in the urban landscape of Kolkata. Their home is right next door to the school, which has been a vibrant centre since its foundation twenty years ago. Embellished with a bold wall mural, it is located beside an open public space, Shibtala Math, where kids play cricket and tanners lay out dyed skins to dry. The air is often full of the shrill cries of circling hawks.

The school's one hundred students, aged four to eighteen, attend local state schools by day, arriving in the evenings and at weekends for tuition in drawing, painting, sculpture and the performing arts. Despite meagre financial resources, Tandra and Pulak have propelled many young people into professional careers in the arts.

During my first stay there, we discussed themes for an arts exchange project linked to the 'green' philosophy of Geddes. Community relationships to rivers, encompassing issues of ecology, water quality, river-borne commerce and ecotourism were the reference points for our first collaboration, 'Language of Rivers and Leaves'.

Language of Rivers and Leaves

Tandra came to Scotland in 2003, the year before the 150th anniversary of the birth of Patrick Geddes. On a visit to his birth-place, Ballater, she became involved in the community's plans to celebrate their town's most famous son. In spring 2004 I went to Bengal to participate in the inception of this ambitious project: a traditional Indian river boat was to be built in Kolkata, decorated with pictograms, prose and poetry linking Geddes and Rabindranath Tagore, and then shipped to Scotland in time for the Geddes celebrations that autumn.

This boat, 18 feet long and weighing 250 kilogrammes, was transported 30 kilometres by rickshaw from the boat-builders' yard to the school, where it provided a curricular framework for creative interpretation of ecological themes through art, music and poetry. Our cross-cultural approach meant sharing understanding of community relationships with rivers in both India and Scotland.

When the boat arrived in Ballater, it brought with it the vivid atmosphere of Bengali festivals and author Bashabi Fraser mounted a programme of pageant, music and dance in a number of Aberdeenshire schools. The formal launch of the boat took place at Loch Kinord on 2 October 2004 – baling furiously, we were just able to raise the red sail of *Sonar Tari* (meaning Golden Boat, inspired by one of Rabindranath Tagore's poems).

That December, we presented a showcase of the project, including an exhibition by the Ballater Group and Aberdeenshire pupils, at the Scottish Parliament, where Green MSP Robin Harper spoke in the Chamber about the relevance of the philosophy of Sir Patrick Geddes.

Sonar Tari is now in 'dry dock' at the Scottish Maritime Museum, Irvine, where a video of the project as it developed in Bengal and the north-east of Scotland can be viewed.

Song of the Rickshaw – Pujas and paradigms for sustainable transport

Success with 'Language of Rivers and Leaves' stimulated a new phase of research. During my third visit to the Art and Craft School in 2005, the monsoon lasted longer than expected. This coincided with the annual festival Durga Puja, when hundreds of brightly painted sculptures of goddess Durga and her family are worshipped and then immersed in the river. The event is cleansing, liberating and very much in the spirit of Hindu philosophy, celebrating birth, death and renewal by uniting with the river as part of the mighty Ganges. Craft 'villages' in the city generate artworks of all sizes in a wave of activity.

On an economic level, this creative ritual ensures that artists and crafts people have a cyclical series of commissions. The clay and bamboo sculptures are left to float away or sink, biodegrading to mix with silt, clay and ashes of human remains; all eventually recycled as part of the chakra of life.

This fabulous and somewhat chaotic festival atmosphere created the backdrop and punctuated the mood of my time in Bengal for a project exploring sustainable modes of transport. The media was reporting that local government was, yet again, considering the decommissioning of the two-wheeled, hand-pulled rickshaw, a mode of transport which some regard as exploitative – man as pack animal, pulling or pedalling heavy loads, in all weathers, with negligible payment.

In the 'Song of the Rickshaw' project, ecological and ethical transport issues were addressed by school pupils in Scotland and India. At the start of the process in Kolkata, two rickshaws were purchased: one tricycle and one two-wheeler. The painting and decorating of the vehicles was exciting and satisfying, despite the wet weather. The pupils adopted the powerful tradition of *Kalighat*, painting and wood-block printing featuring birds, fish and Indian gods. Their designs were meticulous, using powerful graphic treatments and vibrant colour, with floral patterns on the timber bearers and metal chassis. Outlines were created around small feet and these 'carbon' footprints were painted in bright colour onto the footplates of both vehicles.

Model rickshaws were also created and larger painted wooden panels provided individual students with the opportunity to interpret cosmopolitan scenes. These superb panels are now in Scotland and ready to display.

The climax of our endeavours was a public procession in November. The decorated rickshaws were elevated to the status of artworks and lifted onto bamboo trailers with truck axles. The community pageant, featuring brightly coloured flags of Scotland and India, was led by a Bengali Pipe Band. The Mayor of Kolkata attended the evening exhibition and seminar, and a unique song, specially composed for the project, was sung that night. Representatives from local government and Sibdas Ghosh, Professor of Botany, discussed Scotland's relationship with India, the values and challenges of ecotourism and the common need to develop sustainable agriculture, fishing and forestry. The two decorated rickshaws have now been shipped to Aberdeenshire, where they have travelled to schools, energising cultural exchanges.

New projects are evolving. The Mayor of Kolkata has responded with interest to the idea of creating a landscape feature – an 'Indo-Scots meeting point' – at the Maidan, which will highlight the rich publishing heritages of both countries; as part of this project, we hope to restore a historic Scottish printing press – many of which are still to be found in Kolkata – and utilise it to create a collaborative artists' book.

At Aberdeen University on 8 January 2007, as part of the Royal Scottish Geographical Society lecture programme, Kenny Munro will give a talk entitled 'Bengal Boats and Rickshaw Roads'. Full details at www.rsgs.org.

References:
Moorhouse, Geoffrey. *Calcutta*. London: I.B. Tauris, 2005.
Ghosh, Prof. Sibdas (ed). *Ecotourism its Impact on Socio-Economy Heritage and Wild Life Conservation*. Kolkata: The Humboldt Club Calcutta.
Ghosh, Amitav. *Calcutta Chromosome*. London: Harper Perennial, paperback reprint, 2002.
Boardman, Philip. *Worlds of Patrick Geddes: Biologist, Town Planner, Re-educator, Peace Warrior*. London: Routledge, 1978.
Fraser, Dr Bashabi. *Geddes-Tagore Letters*. Rev ed. Edinburgh: Word Power, 2005.
Stephen, Walter (ed). *A Vigorous Institution*. Edinburgh: Luath Press (forthcoming).
Noltie, Henry J. *Indian Botanical Drawings 1793–1866 from the Royal Botanic Garden Edinburgh*. Edinburgh: Royal Botanic Garden, 1999.

Miss Plumb

Hannah Adcock

Isabella Plumb stares out of the photograph, square jaw set, blue-grey eyes locked in a steely gaze on posterity. A set-piece hairstyle is swept up from her wide forehead and her rather thin mouth is tightly compressed. She is almost just an indomitable Victorian matron, except her large ears are pointed at the top, given a slightly fey cast to her otherwise solid features. Miss Plumb (or increasingly Granny Plumb as she became known) never married. She devoted her life to missionary work in India, and in the process travelled nearly twice around the world.

Her archive consists of five boxes of material, predominantly from her adult years. Items include: the diary of her walking tour in the Himalaya mountains as well as one for her round the world trip; reports of mission life; drafts of thirty talks, diaries and correspondence. Mission reports from Sialkot and newspaper articles provide contextual information, whilst material in other hands, such as notes on Eastern architecture and religion, indicate her interest in all aspects of India. Photographs and postcards total 700. The postcards are from all over the world, mementoes of Miss Plumb's adventures on three continents. Miss Plumb is easy to spot in the photos and so are her close relatives, who have similar jaw-lines and ears. Most are unlabelled and captions seldom provide names. Overall, it is an extensive and compelling archive, covering a large proportion of Miss Plumb's long life. I have only scratched the surface but my research continues.

However unusual, ultimately worthy female missionaries have largely failed to capture the interest of historians. Their modesty has been mistaken for insignificance, their evangelising for an embarrassing footnote in the story of empire. Miss Plumb was of her time: as a British woman she believed in a Christian God, as a citizen she believed in empire. Where she differs from the majority of her female contemporaries is that she endured the vicissitudes of a demanding career without the prop of a husband. Today, it can be appreciated that her spiritual mission co-existed with a grass-root campaign for basic women's rights, but she would not have made such a distinction. By the end of her forty-two year career she had overseen the establishment of schools and hospitals, and the arrival of trained female medical staff. 'Miss Plumb forever', wrote a young admirer, just before she was retired by her Scottish employers at the age of sixty-four.

Miss Plumb was born in Mundford in Norfolk in 1861, the youngest daughter of a family of seven children. Her father, James Edward Plumb, died when she was only four months old leaving her mother, Sarah Plumb, sole responsibility for raising the family. Miss Plumb was 'not brought up in the lap of luxury' as she politely writes to a friend. She attended the local school, leaving at the age of fourteen to earn her living: she writes this in a letter, but I have not had time to discover exactly where she went and what she did. Her education clearly did not stop at school. Her speeches about missionary work, mostly delivered when she was home on leave, show a firm grasp of composition; her reading material includes works on Eastern economics. She learnt three languages and her only real linguistic flaw is a tendency to overuse the word 'nice' in her diaries. However, I suspect the word possessed many different shades of meaning for the Victorians.

By her late teens she was in London attending colonial college, as preparation for work in foreign fields. An index for the archive, compiled by a descendant, suggests she began to write essays, including 'The Pilgrim', 'To My Mother' and 'The Working Women's Appeal'. These essays do not appear in the archive. She borrowed £100 to buy books and cover her fees, although she later paid this back 'with pride', as she informed her little grand-niece Elsie Plumb, in a letter dated 1926. From an early age Miss Plumb had wanted to be a missionary, but unlike those whose grand ambitions dwindled with the onset of adulthood, she never wavered from her 'calling'. She writes to Elsie:

God only knows how hard I had to fight in my young days before I was fitted for a worker in the foreign field. Now I have the honour of being the senior lady missionary in the Church of Scotland in India, Africa and China. I did not climb to the top of the tree all at once. It took forty years.

Immured in the belief that God helps those who help themselves, Miss Plumb worked her way up the missionary 'tree' by a combination of hard work, faith and ability. Her determination is underlined by the fact that she resisted pressure to take a different course: when she left for India her mother, aged sixty-two, appears to have been almost inconsolable. No letters to or from her mother survive in the archive, but Miss Plumb writes with great feeling, suggestive of personal experience:

> If there is anything more potent than all others to make us hesitate – to make right appear wrong and a clear duty seem doubtful – it is the grief of all those who eyes are dimmed with age… words, unless well chosen, are not in place at all.

She was twenty-one when she left in 1882. There is no real indication in the archive as to why she chose India or indeed why she worked for the Church of Scotland Women's Association for Foreign Missionaries (Aberdeen Auxiliary). All correspondence places her family firmly in Norfolk. However, she had distant relatives in Scotland and may have spent time with them before attending colonial college. She sometimes uses Scottish words in her correspondence, suggesting at least some immersion in the culture. It is also possible that she was drawn to the Church of Scotland because of its interest in India. Her family knew Maharajah Duleep Singh, heir to the throne of Punjab, which the British annexed from his father in 1849. The Maharajah lived close to the Plumb family home; he owned the Elveden estate, purchased by his trustees in 1863. It can only be imagined what the effect of such a neighbour had on the young Miss Plumb, particularly one who had been converted to Christianity.

Miss Plumb spent her first seven years as a missionary in the city of Poona (Pune), in Western India. She was initially assigned to an orphanage, where she could become accustomed to the children, their languages and their culture. She writes with youthful imagination that India 'seemed almost like fairyland', bursting with colour and vitality, before adding, prosaically, 'if it were not for the noise and dirt'. The rules and regulations she was expected to abide by, as a representative of the Church of Scotland, demanded humble behaviour and unstinting hard work. Paradoxically, at a time when single, educated and independent women were viewed with at least some suspicion, unmarried female missionaries were both accepted and respected. To serve effectively they needed to possess both knowledge and experience: they could study, travel or own property with impunity, provided modesty was preserved. Miss Plumb owned at least two houses in England, possibly inherited after the death of her mother in 1903, and it is faintly amusing to see how her property agent, Henry Boville, had to change the printed 'Mr' on his official letters for a hand written '(M)iss'. The decisive Married Women's Property Act had been passed as recently as 1882. Before that their legal personality had been subsumed into their husbands'.

A short rhyming poem, called 'The Mission Miss Sahibs', captures something of the austerity – and also perhaps the humour – of mission life. This is an extract:

The Mission Miss Sahibs must never complain
Must never be fanciful, foolish and vain
Mission Miss Sahibs must furnish their brain
Of two or three languages knowledge obtain

Apart from the odd fairy fantasy, Miss Plumb seems to have been a model 'Miss Sahib.' After becoming reasonably proficient in Marathi, she began to teach in the outside school and visit zenanas, apartments in a high caste Hindu or Muslim houses where women were kept in seclusion. According to Miss Plumb, these women were rarely allowed to go outside. She quotes the local saying that 'women could not be trusted unless they were dead' as being more than just a misogynistic maxim. This was a severe culture shock for a woman who had just travelled more than 7,000 miles by sea to an unfamiliar country, unescorted. Her response was thoughtful. She wrote that she hoped female missionary work would, in time, 'withdraw from seclusion the wives and mothers of India, making them the companions of husbands and fathers'. In speeches to the general public, given whilst she was on leave in Scotland, she often spoke about the zenanas: 'you know what the life of a Scottish woman is in this country: perfect freedom to go in and out as she chooses; she may speak to whom she likes; she may leave home and go out into the world and choose her own employment and perhaps most importantly for the future happiness and well being of our nation she may choose her own husband.' Miss Plumb begins with the issue of women's freedom and moves swiftly on to how this impacts on the future happiness and well-being of a nation. In many ways her sentiments prefigure later feminist assertions that the personal is political.

It was her conviction that by improving the lot of women in India who were kept in seclusion – she estimated 20 million – the country itself would be incalculably strengthened.

Miss Plumb was assigned to Sialkot (now in Pakistan) in 1889 as the first Aberdeen Auxiliary female representative. This was a resonant area for the Church of Scotland. Its first missionaries to the area had been murdered, along with their baby, during the Indian mutiny of 1857. I imagine Sialkot was a challenging – and alluring – destination for the determined Miss Plumb. Sialkot, with a population of 50,000, had 'a go and swing that makes it most interesting'. The city had the spectacular backdrop of the Himalayas, the 'grandest natural scenery on the globe'. Mr and Mrs Youngson, both experienced missionaries, gave her a warm welcome. She lived with them until 1891 whilst a Women's Mission House was being built. Dr Hutchison and Miss Scorgie were also lodgers and Miss Plumb writes in her diary of long walks, rides and pleasant evenings spent in their company.

Whilst at Sialkot Miss Plumb continued to take a special interest in zenana visiting, often keeping in contact with 'old girls' from mission schools, who typically left at the age of twelve to marry (although not necessarily to cohabit with their husbands). She writes:

> If it is Christ like to go to the sorrowful with sympathy, to bring comfort to the bereaved, to make life a little brighter for a time to some of these secluded prisoners, to help in times of sickness, to whisper hope in the hour of nature's decay, and to point to the Heavenly land and the Friends of Friends; then this is Christ like work.

Miss Plumb waited to be invited to a house to conduct Bible readings, often assisted by a local Christian. One diary entry records how she would first be asked a plethora of secular questions: Why are you not married? Are you going to get married? How long are you going to stay in India? I can only imagine how Miss Plumb would have replied. I assume she brought God into her answer, but I do not know whether the lack of spouse prompted a sigh or a smile. 'Miss Sahibs' did marry, but suitable male missionaries were not in plentiful supply. In times of illness or death in the zenanas, Miss Plumb was resolutely practical, combating an almost visceral dread of the funeral keening of Indian women relatives, and instead offering quiet sympathy and practical tips on nursing. She campaigned tirelessly for qualified women doctors to be sent over to the Sialkot mission. The case, she asserted, was desperate: 'There is a great need for lady doctors. The women have to be satisfied with an untrained native nurse who is both ignorant and stupid.' This is a strong indictment, but Miss Plumb grew up in a society increasingly concerned with public health and its 'correct' management: the 1875 Public Health Act set down in detail what local authorities could do in terms of public health. Conventional Victorian medicine was the yardstick by which Miss Plumb measured attitudes towards health and she would have had little understanding of holistic Indian medical systems such as Ayurveda, already more than 2,000 years old. However, she also based her opinions on specific case studies; on women she had encountered in pain or close to death. She saw first hand how male doctors were denied access to these women, who relied on fathers or husbands to relay their condition to a doctor. The Aberdeen Auxiliary sent out their first female medical missionary to Sialkot in the early 1890s.

Miss Plumb and the medical missionaries gained very few converts, a fact Miss Plumb defended by suggesting what a sacrifice this would entail for an Indian woman – to be cut off from her family, husband and community – and she made a leap of empathy to understand this:

> I often think, that if the condition of things were reversed, and strange teachers from a distant land were to come among us, we and our children would not be so willing to give ourselves up to them, as they are to us.

Whether for her strange dress, stories, intelligence or kindness, Miss Plumb became a welcome guest at many Indian houses. She was asked to take care of two Indian princesses whilst their father was away on business and in her role as guardian, shared zenana with them, which was 'a new experience', as she writes diplomatically. In 1910, more than fifteen years later, she visited the two princesses in another of their homes, deep in the jungle of Oudh. Although only able to stay for the day, she endured twenty-eight miles on an elephant with a bed attached to its back, to reach their home. She writes, 'It was no easy matter to hold up an umbrella with one hand, while I grasped the bedstead with the other to keep myself from falling off.' It is rather hard not to laugh, particularly given that on her return journey a dozen men with sticks and scowling faces accompanied her for about a mile. They had presumably never before seen a well-built white woman perched perilously on an elephant. Humour aside, however, Miss Plumb was sincerely attached to the two ladies and their father and perhaps it was this, her great capacity for kindness, that caused her to be held in affection by Indian men and women – despite her strange religion and perplexing, unmarried state.

Miss Plumb seems to have become, if anything, even more adventurous with age. She made a 400-mile walking tour in the Himalaya Mountains in 1908, aged forty-seven. The tour began in Chamba, the capital of a native principality where the respected medical missionary Dr Hutchison was head of the mission. He was to accompany Miss Plumb and her companion, Miss Browne, on their 'holiday', which began with a three-day walk over the Sach Pass, 14,328 feet above sea level. Miss Plumb describes some of the difficulties:

> The descent was much more difficult than the ascent. There was no visible path – nothing but a wide expanse of snow. A postman who overtook us helped me for a few yards; then his foot slipped, and he slid down the mountain side – fortunately, he was able to stop himself before reaching the rocks below. Five men had tried to cross this pass in the Spring: two perished; the other three, after struggling on for five days without food, required to have parts of their frost-bitten limbs cut off – an operation performed by the village blacksmith.

Miss Plumb's expedition escaped unscathed and continued onwards to Kilar, Sanch, 'Sensation Summit', Kyelang, Tindi and the Drati Pass. Miss Plumb retained Victorian dress throughout, although Dr Hutchison thoughtfully provided her with Indian shoes called chaplis. Small feasts were instrumental in maintaining her physical (and psychological) strength: 'the Doctor and I had scones and cheese before we got to the top which refreshed us'. They often camped wild at night, with Miss Plumb showing typical fortitude. She writes at one point that she slept well 'despite bears.' In subsequent years Miss Plumb visited Japan, China, Canada and America, before travelling home to Britain, where she suffered a nasty bout of flu, brought on by over exertion. She chose to give more than 100 lectures on her return, rather than recuperating from her exertions. Her last grand journey was in 1928, a pilgrimage to the Holy Land that took her to Baghdad, Damascus, Beirut, Jerusalem and Egypt. By this time Miss Plumb was retired. A notice to this effect appeared in the *News of Women's Missions* in 1925, accompanied by a photograph of Miss Plumb looking more than usually implacable:

> At the time of [Miss Plumb's] entrance in office there was no Mission House, only two native female missionaries, and hardly any organisation; whereas now the Mission has a commodious official residence, a staff of five lady missionaries from Scotland, and about a score of native women teachers and other workers; two well-attended schools; a Missionary Boarding House to provide Christian teachers for the schools of the

Punjab, visitations of the zenanas within, and the villages around the city; a woman's hospital; a Christian 'Memorial Townlet'; and a rest home where missionaries on holiday receive needful temporary rest and a comfortable home.

Miss Plumb seems to have been ambivalent about retirement, writing to Elsie in the early 1920s that she longed to see her in England. But she remained in India for five years after retiring, superintending the Wyligh rest home in Dalhousie, for which she had campaigned tirelessly. This was a job that she undertook voluntarily and without much obvious recognition from the Aberdeen Auxiliary. However, her services were greatly appreciated by visitors of all ages. Her youthful vigour captured their playful spirits and on her '21st birthday' (when she was sixty-six) she was presented with a photo album complete with captions. One photograph shows her seated in an inelegant, sedan-style chair; the caption reads 'she who rules at Wyligh'. A poem composed for her sixty-first birthday also writes of her 'in climbing, hiking, traipsing, to make the rest all run'. It also says (I think): 'And when the man of eighty comes may both be in the mood. Three cheers for our Miss Plumb.'

This may well have been an in-joke, and a later hand suggests her friend Professor Scorgie as a candidate for the 'man of eighty'. However, I did unearth marriage banns dated 1929 and the gentleman in question was Dr Hutchison whom she had known since the early 1890s. In 1929 he was eighty-four, and died soon after. It is easy to spin a romantic narrative about a love affair thwarted by duty, but I really haven't found any evidence. The most resonant part of the document, in my opinion, was a description of Miss Plumb. She had become a 'spinster', a word that didn't seem to apply to her when she was active as a missionary. In contrast, Dr Hutchison, despite his advanced years, was described as a 'missionary'.

Miss Plumb returned to Britain in 1930 to live at 'The Retreat', the Plumb family home and she met her great-nephew Edward for the first time. He remembers her as a 'great person' who taught him 'about manners and how to treat people'. After her death from cancer in 1944, he received many calls from people who had been her friend, keen to discuss her kindness or her influence on the political and social life of the Punjab. With his donation of her archive to the National Library of Scotland, a window has opened onto her legacy: her role as an intrepid traveller; her campaign for the provision of schools, female doctors, hospitals and basic human rights for women. She was certainly modest, but far from insignificant: 'Miss Plumb forever', I say.

Isabella Plumb in the community

Isabella Plumb

TOP: Missionary group

BELOW: Isabella Plumb's study

FACING PAGE: A page from Isabella Plumb's journal

overtake. In some we are
listened to from the first;
and have every opportunity
of explaining to the women
our message. In others they
are curious about us; they
have many questions to ask.
Why are you not married?
Are you going to be married?
How long are you going to
stay in India? And then
they want to examine our
dress; and compare it with
their own. It is sometimes
trying to submit to all this
minute inspection, but one
has to be patient, and by
and bye their curiosity is
satisfied, and they sit down
to listen. Some of the women
in the zenanas are very

In Economy

Rajorshi Chakraborti

The man beside me was scratching his balls, openly, brazenly, although he was sandwiched between two strangers, and numerous others were still moving down the aisle. His fly was wide open in the shape of an eye, and he was busy in there with all the bunched-up fingers of his right hand, face down, gaze focused. Yes, true, I had been abroad for five years, and I needed reminding about the incredible degrees of Indian frankness regarding all bodily matters and discharges, but this surely wouldn't stupefy just me. I wasn't strolling along Dhakuria Lake, on the bank adjacent to the railway line slums: we were in an aeroplane, at Muscat airport, this fellow was an international passenger.

I fixed my stare towards the opposite seats, until he had soothed his discomfort to full satisfaction. The chap by the window seemed equally oblivious, his head stuck in the in-flight magazine duty-free section. Was it indeed me who had become so squeamish? Perhaps flights were the new buses, at least those that travelled to the Gulf – I wondered, looking up and down to get a better idea of my co-passengers (and truthfully, in the faint hope of a vacant seat) – in the sense that this one seemed full of characters you would only ever see in buses before, especially rural ones.

What made my predicament truly perilous was that I'd run out of reading matter. As usual, I'd underestimated, believing like an idiot that I would spend a fair portion of either flight asleep, or at least, a few of the movies would be bearable. But all my life, I'd been a mile-high insomniac, and so there I was, desperately clutching onto the opened page of the *Herald Tribune*, determined to continue with business, sport and obituaries after that, anything to avoid conversing with Mr Itch-Guard until I could bolt immediately after take-off.

But here again, I'd underrated the cunning and agility required to bend the law to your purposes in my native land, how briefly any opportunity lasts, how many competitors there are eyeing whatever it is you secretly desire. London must have really softened me – it was being demonstrated over and over even before we'd touched down in Calcutta. And besides, I was still getting accustomed to the idea of this lot taking over a plane. How could I compete with the eagle-eyed resolve and who-gives-a-fuck audacity of champions who travelled usually on the tops of buses or hanging by their toes from suburban trains? No one could have accused me of being tardy in searching for another place as soon as the seat-belt signs went off, but within that minimum pocket of time, all the rows I'd spotted as empty in the rear and moved delightedly towards, had been seized already, and their new occupants were stretched out full-length, armrests raised, apparently fast asleep to elude any argument. And what argument could there be, since their right to usurp empty seats was as valid as mine?

Things deteriorated upon my shamefaced return. I clung resolutely to the earlier strategy of devouring the *Tribune* as if I would be attending an IAS exam on current affairs directly after landing. But very soon, the fidgeter was up to something novel. He'd placed his cushion upon the armrest that I had readily surrendered just to avoid contact with the hand that had scratched the noodle, and was now employing his blanket vigorously to wipe his arm. The white cushion was already stained a light brown. With gravest misgivings I faced him finally as if to request an explanation, because this was simply too much, but instead of pointing downwards as I'd grit my teeth to expect, he gestured towards the lights and the luggage bins. And this time, I had to concede a misjudgement. I'd wronged him just this once. A fairly regular brown drip – that could have been diluted grease or dirty water, something I'd never seen before in an aircraft (though often enough on an Indian bus) – which originated near the console for switches and lights, was indeed falling straight upon the armrest between us, and had been staining the pillow and his shirt.

'*Dekhun na Pepsi ki na?*' he implored, as if it was odd of me not to have risen already.

It seemed distant enough from the door of the bin for it not to be leaking cola, but there was a slim possibility. Yet there was nothing that looked like a bottle visible among the bags. Everything was sealed and the drip clearly had another source.

'*Aami air-hostess ke dakchhi, daran,*' and I pressed the button to summon her.

Yet though she could neither solve nor explain the problem, she seemed entirely tranquil while considering the scenario that our mid-air pressurised cabin might have sprung a leak, and simply suggested, heels already turned around, that we shift seats, since it was a far-from-full flight.

Something diabolical as well as wildly optimistic within me noted and capitalised upon my opportunity.

'She's right. Many seats empty behind us. You should move immediately. Look, it has stained your shirt'.

Why he didn't take to this suggestion beats me. He frowned and shook his head. Conversation stalled. I spent the next few minutes making sure I didn't re-occupy the armrest by mistake. I was wearing a warm golden shirt, of unconscionable price, but I'd picked it up at a Harvey Nick's sale. Three years on, contemplating the bargain still suffused me with pleasure.

Not half an hour had passed before he was at it again. So blatantly, as if he was squatting by the railway tracks, facing away from the overflowing trains. He unbuttoned himself, stuck in his hoof, felt his jewels cautiously, and then scratched as if there'd been a mosquito inside. Yes, yes, I know, but how could I not have noticed? In fact, since Itch-Guard was leaning forward, I actually looked across to see if the fellow by the window was as perturbed as me. Perhaps together, egging one another on through eye-contact, one of us could broach the awful subject.

But he was already fast asleep, and since he was evidently from the same class as Mr Minor Sexual Misdemeanour, I imagined he would have been sanguine even if he'd witnessed everything, twice. I want to clarify, vis-à-vis my countrymen, I was no prude. Five years away cannot soften a shell acquired over a lifetime. I was hardened to the projectile spitting, the copious clearing of noses and other orifice-exploring, the non-alcoholic belching and the preparatory hawking, the tubercular fits of coughing. But this weed had lowered the bar.

Finally, I felt compelled to draw attention to the matter somehow, however obliquely.

'Do you want to visit the bathroom?'

'No, it's no use,' he replied. 'It doesn't go away. In fact, I feel worse when I return.'

A mystifying response: I momentarily forgot I was supposed to be annoyed.

'Aren't you well?'

'No, I had an accident. Since then I'm in constant pain. To sit still is an agony, I can't walk very far any more, and in the toilet it burns even worse.'

'What happened?' I asked, facing him for the first time directly, looking upward from what I realised had been a near constant stare in the direction of his groin. He must have found *me* odd. He was ordinary to look at, perhaps thirty, not unpleasant or hostile, rendered slightly pitiful in light of his predicament. I wasn't angry any more, not after I heard the word 'accident'.

'You know how we have two balls each,' he explained without a flicker in his expression, calling them seeds, which is the colloquial Bengali term. 'A crane pierced my bag and damaged one of them. It took twenty-three stitches to join. They were removed day before yesterday, but it hasn't healed well.'

'A forklift crane?' was all I could think of asking, by way of continuation, as if it was vital to be sure! My face had scrunched in horror as he spoke, factually and without overt self-pity.

He nodded. I turned away in shock, and perhaps to work up a better comeback. I wanted to hear more, where he worked, what the hospitals were like, what he was going home to.

It was he who resumed with a non-sequitur. 'Please excuse my Bengali. You know, I'm a full-fledged Bengali. But living there, you speak so many languages, Hindi, English, even the occasional Arabic where you have to, so suddenly it's hard to switch back. But I speak Bengali perfectly. Please don't mind, do you?'

'The same thing happens to me,' I replied bemusedly. 'It also takes me a while to get used to Bangla. Don't worry, after a day or so, it'll all flow back. So you picked up some Arabic while you were there?'

'Yes, a few expressions. Some people don't speak English so well. And if I'd known some more, it would have been useful at the hospital to explain my problems. I couldn't really tell them in English.'

'Are the hospitals free? Was the treatment alright?'

'Yes, they're free, but I think cat and dog hospitals are in better condition. They did the basic dressing and stitches, but that's why I'm going home. The pain has increased, because they didn't have time to understand what I was saying.'

'It'll be better at home. You'll have a familiar doctor to whom you can explain your symptoms freely, and you can recover in your own house, with loved ones to look after you.'

'I had no other option. I can't lift anything so I haven't been able to work since the accident. And the company would only provide a ticket home by way of compensation, so that's all I could do.'

After a while he spoke again. 'You might form the wrong impression from my clothes.' He wasn't wearing exceptional clothes by any standards, just a cotton shirt and trousers, socks and 'duplicate' white Reebok trainers, which reminded me momentarily of Jerry Seinfeld. 'And this watch,' holding out a fake Casio digital, 'is a fake. You have to wear something special for those who'll come to the airport, after a year and a half. But I'm returning empty-handed. I had to borrow money from friends even to buy a few things. Some cosmetics for my family from the airport, and a few utensils. Nothing more.'

It was slightly later, when he used the expression again to inform me that his 'family' was completing a teacher-training certificate to qualify for a job in a school, that I recognised he meant his wife. 'But surely they'll understand the situation, in what circumstances you were forced to return. There's always time later for presents. First priority is your health.'

'I haven't confided in anyone yet. With what face shall I tell them? I borrowed a lakh to pay the agent to go to Dubai, and now I'm home after just eighteen months, empty-handed, having thrown away my job. Even today I won't be able to say a word. They will have rented a car to come all the way from the village; we'll return to a big lunch; neighbours will visit; everyone will ask questions. Maybe tomorrow, when I have some time alone with my family.'

Two unworthy thoughts passed through my head at this point, at differing rates: one was light-hearted and sped through, and the other lingered and assumed a more definite shape. Surely his 'family' would find out the first few minutes they were alone, that he was for the moment an 'oddball'. (Appalling, I know). And then I wondered if he was a practised swindler, and this was an elaborate routine. I decided to be on my guard for a while, perhaps slightly stand-offish once more. But what an accomplished master, if he was indeed a trickster. He'd added fine details to the routine, even donating the lamb and the mishti from his meal to his other neighbour – because he claimed to have no appetite and to be eating simply for sustenance – who through all this had himself been a remarkable study in avoidance. (Accomplices?) He appeared not to have registered a word of our exchange. Oh, and Santosh Biswas, that was his name, had also re-buttoned his fly.

And yet, the shifting in the seat, the periodic winces of discomfort: what if they were authentic? How much money was I obliged to offer, in the event of his sincerity? Because then it wasn't a matter of his asking; rather I myself should step forward. But what kind of sum could begin to tide him over his troubles? A token gesture would be next to useless. He had personal debts, loans to human traffickers, and for starters, presents to pick up hastily in the Calcutta duty-free. Jesus!

Should my offer of help merely cover the gifts? Would that be generous enough?

However, once the trays were removed, Santosh shifted the conversation to other matters, reminding me first not to use the armrest, even by mistake. He told me about taking the taxi to the supermarket to buy his weekly provisions, which brought to his mind the insane speeds at which people drove on the highways of Dubai. There seemed to be no rules or limits. He warned me (in the event of visiting) that I was asking to be killed if I ever slowed down or stopped without ample warning: the cars behind would have no way of braking in time and would slam headlong into mine. Such incidents invariably culminated in a gigantic fireball, it appeared. In a year and a half, he'd witnessed four.

At this point, his discomfort became unbearable, and he departed for the toilet. I returned to my seat and continued trying to make up my mind about him, about which of the roads in the forest to choose: the path of credulity or that of cynicism.

When he returned I asked him to describe the accident. In fact, to cloak my real motive (the testing of his back-story), I asked him more generally about work conditions on construction sites.

'I have been very lucky before. In fact, I should already be dead. Last year I was high up on the scaffolding near the twenty-first floor of a tower, carrying some massive window panes, when one of those huge gusts of wind that are common at such heights nearly blew me off my feet. I was at a corner, so I couldn't move, nor could I rest my load. God knows how I held on.'

'You mean there's no requirement to wear safety harnesses?'

He shook his head briskly as if to swat off the obvious, and continued, 'and yet this time, my feet were firmly planted on the ground. In fact, I was working below ground-level on a small masonry job. The forklift driver insisted afterwards he couldn't see me down there. Another inch and he would have ripped out my scrotum.' He called it his 'whole thing'.

To change the subject I asked about his housing situation. He claimed to be a teetotaller, but revealed the primary cause that drove most of his friends to drink excessively in the evenings was the ordeal of calling home. 'The only thing anyone is interested in: when and how much are you sending? And an unending list of emergencies and demands. No one asks how we manage there, what we do, about our ups and downs. They have their fixed image of life in Dubai, fast cars, gold, electronics and air-conditioned luxury. This constant pressure leads to all that drinking.

'But they're good lads. Three of them helped me out with two thousand dirhams after the accident. Somehow I have to return, because they lent the money on trust. I don't want them to believe I tricked them.'

At this point I grew silent to gather my thoughts. My doubts had vanished: I just couldn't absorb so much detail while listening. I still didn't know how to extend a hand spontaneously, beyond repeating what I'd said already, that I was a great believer in God and Providence (now who was dissembling?), and that this trip home had been the right choice. He could recover with the care of his family, and return healthy and restored. God had averted a much worse disaster, though of course, I could not ask if he knew how bad the internal damage was. But the extent of his worries truly awed me, dwarfing at that moment even my own: his health, his debts, his family, his future as a worker and as a man. I was arriving in the aftermath of a catastrophe; he was landing in the next phase of one.

Yet I had been en-route for fifteen hours straight, and it was only the plane touching down at Dum Dum that awoke me from the snooze into which I'd inadvertently slumped. I noticed he was awake and looking forward without any particular expression. There wasn't much to say before leaving the aircraft, and the next thing I had to do was hurriedly fill out the landing card while waiting in the queue at immigration. That was when he approached me once more, with a request to fill up his form, because he said his hands were too shaky. I showed him where he had to sign, and noted that the date of birth in his passport was dubious. Come on, Santosh had been twenty-four well into the last millennium.

I was fortunate with my bags this once, and before exiting, pushed my trolley over towards him to shake his hand. He had an unusual favour to seek. Nothing to do with money: he wanted me to sign a small pocket-book as a memento, as if I was a celebrity he'd encountered.

I don't know what prompted me to include Baba's address in Calcutta, where I'd be staying, along with my 'autograph'. I honestly cannot account for it. And soon afterwards, when I spotted Baba among the crowd outside the airport and began paying attention to all the urgent, painful stuff he had to update me on, there seemed to be no call on my part to intrude with Santosh's story. And it remained thus throughout that stay: one hurtling event upon another, and no one ever asked me how my flight to Calcutta had been.

Kali

Margaret Burnett

The whole way to the station in the rickshaw I had to sit with my bum half off the slippery red plastic seat and hold on to the little metal arm rest in case I got bounced out as we jolted over the holes in the road. Dad sat beside me with his legs crossed and his arms folded, looking about him at the busy streets, completely unaware of my predicament. For a thin man, he took up a surprising amount of space. We passed Gobindu, the College electrician in his khaki uniform, buying cigarettes at a paan seller's. He salaamed us, smiling cheerfully amongst the crowd of young men in tight white trousers. Dad returned his salaam gravely. 'Where are you going?' Gobindu asked me in Bengali. 'Calcutta,' I called after him as the rickshaw bumped into Queenie Street. He was curious to see Dad and me on our own together.

We went past the shabby, curtained doorway that led into the photographer's studio in the Muslim section of the bazaar. I had had my photo taken there last year for my new passport because I had turned sixteen and couldn't be in Mum's any more. I remembered looking at the little black and white photo shyly as the girl in it had looked shyly at me. The girl had long, thick hair tied half-back so it was off her face, and her face was round and young. She had dark eyes and Dad's heavy, non-womanly eyebrows and his high forehead too. She was smiling a hesitant smile as if not sure what happened after sixteen.

Dad moved beside me and I turned to him, but he was just waving flies away from his face. Last night, he had come out of his study and leaned stiff-armed on the back of his blue chair in the sitting room.

'Would you like to go to Calcutta tomorrow, Fiona?' he asked me.

I was packing books in the bottom of my red trunk. It was always strange when Dad said my name, like getting a little glimpse of somebody else. 'With you?'

'Only if you want to.'

He was making this gesture because we wouldn't be seeing each other for a long time. I was leaving India with Mum as I'd finished school and it was time for me to carry on with my life in Britain. Dad was staying on for two more years and then he would be joining us.

I smiled at him politely. 'That would be nice.'

There was a tiny pause.

'Where would you like to go?' he asked.

'I don't mind.' And I really didn't. Everywhere I went these days, I gathered images to take away with me, I stored them inside me like padding, as if I didn't know who I'd be in the foreign country that was Britain.

'Well, we could maybe go and see the Kali Temple. Do you fancy that?'

'We could be tourists,' I said, smiling. Living here as we did, we'd hardly seen any tourist sites.

'Yes,' he said seriously. There was another pause and then he gave a little nod and returned to his study.

But my heart had sunk. What would we say to each other, alone together for the whole day? Going out with him when I was small had been different. Whenever I saw his clean, white, long-fingered hand hanging by his side, I'd skip up to him and take it, as if its emptiness was an invitation. Sure, he was stern and could get frighteningly angry. But he was my Dad. But as I grew up, he became more and more remote, leaving me to Mum. I guess he didn't know what to do with me once I developed breasts and started my periods. He didn't know how to treat these things, as if he wasn't sure if they were a part of me, and if so, what should he do with them? Actually, that was pretty much my problem too.

Going past the old Portuguese church, where saris were stretched out to dry along the broken metal railings, Dad finally spoke. 'Have you heard from any of your friends yet?'

'It's a bit soon.'

'Yes, I suppose so.'

We waited to see if anything more could be said about that.

The rickshaw turned into the Grand Trunk Road, ignoring a lorry that bore down on us, its horn blaring. The rickshaw driver, a skinny old man, pulled with all his effort on the handlebars to get some weight onto the pedals, and we continued safely. In the chemist's, where I went with Mum sometimes to get aspirins or the malaria pills that we took every morning, people clamoured at the counter with their prescriptions held out like little white flags.

'Are they all travelling to America?' Dad asked finally.

'That's right.'

'Going straight there?'

We went over the crossroads where nobody paid any attention to the policeman in big, khaki shorts waving his arms on his podium in the middle. His frowning face was half-scared as he blew his whistle.

'Some of them are going via Japan.'

'I see.' He scratched the side of his mouth, then folded his arms again. 'And then starting university,' he said, as if to conclude the picture.

'Yes. Most of them, anyway.'

He laughed in assent. 'Like you, in fact.'

But we didn't know yet if the British universities would accept my American High School Diploma which I'd got from my mission boarding school up in the mountains in Mussoorie. I'd gone there because it had taken me as far as I could go with my education in India, further than the British missionary school in Darjeeling which just took you till sixteen. And now even this had come to the end, like travelling down a rope and finding that it had run out in mid-air, and all I could do was let go.

'Like I hope to do,' I said.

Dad leaned his body towards me, his arms still folded, and gave a little nod and a smile, his heavy eyebrows raised in acknowledgement. He always made me feel clever when he did that, as if we had come to the same conclusion. We were silent for the rest of the way, which was good, I could hide the turmoil and fear that the thought of university always threw up.

We came into the lane where the dhobi lived and I caught a glimpse of his long, sad, hard-done-by face in the dark room of his house, ironing. His children laughed up at us from the doorway. It was strange to think that this would all carry on next week. I'd be gone, but their lives would be the same. I couldn't imagine that, it didn't seem real. And it started off that feeling I carried with me these days, a splintered, painful weight that scraped as it turned about inside me. It was high up in my chest, as if it was trying to get out but was too big.

On the train, Dad and I stood in the crush, sweat trickling down our faces and necks. His head and shoulders were above everybody, his stern face calm, his grey eyes glancing around in an interested, alert way as if he was in the crowd but apart from it at the same time. Not like me, squashed and self-conscious. He managed to manoeuvre his hand into his trouser pocket, bring out a white, folded handkerchief, wipe his face, and return the hanky to his pocket. A man with a thin moustache who was squeezed up next to him said something, and Dad nodded, laughing. I was always proud of him, with his military bearing, and his high, white forehead, like a wall behind which he stored his integrity.

The train passed green rice fields and the flat-roofed jumble of buildings of the towns that lined the Hooghly river all the way to Calcutta. When it stopped at stations, the surge of people pushed me further and further into the carriage. A young woman sitting down was knitting and I watched her needles, deft and quick. She had a big moon face and enormous, placid eyes. The Bengalis thought moon-faced women were beautiful. Images of Kali usually had a huge, round face, although I wouldn't exactly have called her beautiful. She was everywhere in West Bengal. She had a black face and body and her naked breasts were covered by a garland of decapitated heads, and she wore a little skirt of chopped-off arms. Her red tongue hung out and her eyes were wide and staring, and in her hands she carried knives and swords. I wondered what the woman knitting thought of her, what Kali meant to her, this goddess who was the complete opposite of how women were supposed to be.

I was pushed against the woman and I kicked her by mistake. Kicking someone in West Bengal was a terrible insult and I leaned down to touch her feet in apology. But, knitting away, she smiled at me and didn't seem to mind. Kali probably would have chopped my head off. Even so, I liked Kali, I liked her being different. I liked that she could chop people's heads off.

At Howrah station, we joined the throng of hurrying people under the high, wide, bird-filled roof of the station, all making for the buses. 'This way,' Dad said, pointing to the side door where the minibuses were. We got a minibus and, crouching uncomfortably under the low roof as we stood pressed inside it, we crossed Howrah bridge, as packed as our bus, and drove into Calcutta. When Dad raised his eyebrows to me as a signal and pushed his way to the door, I followed.

We were at the Esplanade. People walked with their heads down, skirting huge dirty puddles from a broken drain. A cow stood in one, rubbish floating around its legs, chewing the husk of a green coconut. Dad brushed flies away from his face. 'This way,' he said. 'We need another bus.'

We crossed a side road and approached the plate glass window of the Air India offices. For a second I couldn't think who these two Europeans were walking along the street, both rather shabby and insignificant-looking amongst the crowd of Bengalis, the man very upright, with short hair and a high forehead, the girl in a long, red and white batik skirt, with long, thick hair in a middle parting, and an unattractive frown on her big, round face. My God, it was us. No wonder Mum was always telling me to smile. I thought I looked wild and free, but I just looked as if I was trying to figure out, crossly, where to go.

'Can we go to the university area?' I suddenly asked.

'Which university?'

I didn't know there was more than one. 'Calcutta.'

He hesitated. 'What for?'

I had visions of young men in white kurtas sitting around old wooden tables in tea shops, arguing and shouting and laughing in the excitable Bengali way, and young women pulling up chairs and joining in. I wanted to look as a way of reassuring myself.

'To look around.'

He turned to glance behind him as if it was in that direction. 'Maybe another day,' he said.

He was terrible at changing plans. Mum could turn on a fifty paisa piece, but Dad was like one of those oil tankers at sea that took a mile to stop. We were bound for the Kali Temple so that was where we would go.

'There isn't another day,' I said. I looked at a dusty shop window with faded, sun-bleached tins of dried baby milk in it, pretending to be interested, nearly overcome by tears by this terrible fact.

'Hmm?' Dad said, heading for the tangle of traffic at the Maidan, as if he hadn't quite heard me. We crossed over tram lines, wound our way through vendors and the smell of the chunna and moori that they were selling, and dodged buses, rickshaws and cycles. A man pulling a cart piled high with empty Dalda tins got between me and Dad, and Dad paused to wait for me. At the bus stop, he glanced down at my face as if there was something in it. What had he seen? I never knew how much my face gave away of what I was thinking.

We didn't speak again till we got off the bus at Kalighat. A strange, square, curved white roof rose above trees.

'Do you know why she has her tongue out?' Dad asked as we walked towards it.

'No,' I said. Actually, I did, but I knew by his tone that he wanted to tell me. It was odd talking with Dad about tongues, uncomfortable, really. Tongues were for kissing. I'd discovered that briefly and wonderfully with Paul, and then, several months later, frantically, tremblingly, troublingly, with Jim.

'Well,' Dad said, 'she went on a rampage once, killing and slicing heads off, that kind of thing, and no one could stop her. She was in a kind of trance, she was enjoying herself so much. They didn't know what to do, she was too powerful for them. Then Shiva had the answer.' Dad lifted his long forefinger to make the point. He loved good answers to problems. 'Trick her into putting her foot onto his body, then she'd stop. And that's what happened.'

He paused, as if he'd come to the end too soon.

'And she stuck her tongue out in shame,' I said, helping him with his story.

'That's right.'

'Do you know why she's worshipped?' I asked.

He hesitated, biting his lower lip, smiling. 'No, actually, I don't. And I can't imagine, either.'

'Neither can I,' I said, and we laughed together guiltily.

'Do we go this way, do you think?' he asked. 'Do you think so? I think it must be.'

It began to get fun. I liked it when Dad and I laughed together, sharing something. He stood amongst the milling people and pointed past rows of shops selling garlands of marigolds piled high in baskets. The hot, humid air was filled with their cool scent.

We walked up wide, shallow steps to what looked like the entrance, and left our sandals alongside hundreds of others. All those sandals were troubling but I didn't have time to think about that as we followed where others were going.

I'd never been in a temple before, but I'd passed many and had had a quick look inside. They seemed quiet, peaceful places where people sat around, not doing anything in particular. This one wasn't like that at all. People streamed in from all sides. As we went further in, the streams merged into a frightening torrent until we were pushed helplessly into a big hall. Kali stood above us at the far end with her black body and red tongue and her garland of heads. We were crammed into the middle of a crowd of shouting, yelling, frenzied people, all trying to thrust their way to the front. I struggled to stay back but it was no good, I was being pushed to the front. A woman's damp arm seemed glued to mine, pinned down in the crush, I could even feel the hairs on it. She shouted her prayers, her face intent, her mouth wide open. I couldn't make out what she was shouting for the noise. On my other side a man's shoulder was shoved up against mine, he was trying to raise his hand and it got caught in the folds of my skirt. In front of me, a fat man had a brass plate lifted over his head, piled with fruit, and he struggled to stay upright. I smelled bananas and the sickening, too-sweet smell of over-ripe mangoes. Above us showers of marigold heads were being thrown to Kali, who stood there, her tongue out and her eyes staring, taking it all in, as if there was room for plenty more.

I swivelled my head, searching for Dad. He was a little behind me, leaning backwards, his eyes white, like a shying horse. A rushing, choking, jumbled feeling of exaltation came over me, seeing him out of control. Good. Good. But I felt a terrible pity too, as if I'd seen him naked. He saw me and nodded his head toward the archways at the side. We shoved our way there, grim and determined, using our elbows as if we were getting off a commuter train.

Space – sudden emptiness. We stood, shaken, squinting in the sunshine, not looking at each other. 'Let's try this way,' Dad said, attempting to assert himself. We went around a corner into a court yard shaded by a tree. A small group like a family was huddled around something. An older woman's hollow-cheeked face was deeply concentrated, her pan-stained mouth a thin red line. Peering between their legs, I saw a little white goat. A plump man in a white dhoti and a Bhramin's thread across his smooth, naked back bent over the goat. He had a large knife in his hand and he cut the goat's throat. I didn't see the cutting, just the bright red blood collected neatly in a brass bowl held by a squatting boy, and the four stick-like legs suddenly collapsing.

My own legs felt weak. We turned around and walked quickly to the front, Dad finally admitting defeat.

'Did you look?' he asked, as we collected our sandals.

'A little. I didn't see its throat cut though. Did you?'

'Yes, I did.' He was rather pale, his eyes uncertain, his shoulders sagging. 'Did you know they did things like that?'

'No, I've never even heard of it.'

'Neither have I.'

We stopped uncertainly at the bottom of the steps, Dad still not his usual I'm-in-charge-here self. I breathed in the smell of marigolds to try and steady myself. The reassuring noises of Calcutta were all around us, cars and buses sounded their horns, cycle bells jangled, people walking by talked loudly to each other, and a radio played film music from one of the open-fronted marigold shops. And above it all was the sound of birds – singing, calling, chattering, cawing.

A barefoot little boy in a torn shirt emerged from a group of men outside a tea shop.

'Tourist?' he asked us.

'No, no,' we both assured him.

'Tourist,' he insisted, looking at us impassively. 'Mother Teresa,' he said, and gestured beyond some trees. 'Mother Teresa, five rupees.'

'One rupee,' Dad said. I knew he had been wondering what to do next and this seemed to be the answer. She was a relief, actually, we knew all about her.

'Three rupees, Sahib.'

'Two rupees,' Dad said.

The boy assented with a slight sideways shake to his head. We followed him for a minute until he stopped in front of a low red-brick building and stood with his hands behind his back. The green board above the doorway said, Mother Teresa's Home for Dying Destitutes. The double doors were open and we took a few wary steps forward. There were four long rows of wooden rope-strung beds and very thin old men lying or sitting on them. A nun in a white sari walked about calmly in the silence. Her serenity was disconcerting. A man sitting on the bed next to the door, his arced body as thin as a brown blade of grass, regarded us as if from a long way away.

'Go in,' the boy said in Bengali. 'Have a look.'

Oh God, no, please no. I couldn't go in and look at dying people. It would be like stepping off into empty space. What would they think, being stared at? And how would they look at me? But to my relief, Dad paid him for his services, a chastened expression on his face, and we left quickly. 'You didn't want to see any more, did you?' he asked.

'No, that's all right.'

'Well, shall we go home?'

It was as if we'd come as far as we could, there wasn't anywhere else to go. I looked around me. 'All right,' I said reluctantly.

But he hesitated and stopped, looking around him as well. The hesitation went on and on, not like him, and I wondered what was coming. It was friendly, standing like this with him while he was vague and uncertain. I liked him when he showed his weaker side, he became almost pally then. He looked down at me as if considering something and our eyes met. He gave an embarrassed grimace, his mouth twisting into what was meant to be a smile. 'Hmmgh,' he grunted, his eyes going shifty, as if I'd caught him in a trap. Then he coughed, clearing the phlegm from his throat and we carried on walking until we reached the bus stop.

'Have you heard of St Augustine?' he asked, looking down the road as we stood on the dusty pavement. Other people waited around us. The men held folded newspapers, and some young children in school uniforms had satchels on their backs like the one I had worn every day going to primary school in the rickshaw.

'Vaguely,' I said. The nun must have set him thinking of theological matters. Or maybe he was trying to gather his world around him again after it got shook up by Kali.

He told me about him, and I was interested and asked him questions which he loved answering, all about the early church, and what came first, belief or understanding. This was Augustine's big thing, seemingly. We stood in the shade of a bunyan tree, its heart shaped leaves hanging limply in the heat.

'What does come first?' I asked.

'Oh, belief. Once you have that, then you understand. You can't understand without it.'

'Do you think that?'

'Oh yes. Reason only tells you so much.' He put his hands in his pockets and jingled the change, his eyes charged with energy, as if there was much more that he couldn't say. It was funny, Dad seemed to live in reason. I couldn't imagine him letting go into belief.

'Of course, Augustine articulated feelings,' he continued.. 'He was well-known in the ancient world for that – it was pretty unusual at the time.'

'Oh.' And yet Dad couldn't do that at all. Maybe that was why he liked Augustine. Maybe that was why his eyes went so frighteningly fierce sometimes, as if there was too much feeling inside him.

A bus came but I was glad it wasn't ours, I liked talking to Dad like this. The children climbed on, their satchels disappearing amongst the bodies crowding the door.

'St Augustine had a very clear position on sex,' he said, looking at the row of ramshackle shops across the road. A mechanic was mending an old motor bike on the pavement, revving the engine to a high pitch. 'It was his view that the sex drive was both good and bad.'

'Oh.' I tried to sound casual. Mum had told me about sex when I was eleven and had started my periods. But Dad had never mentioned it before. I was puzzled. Why was he telling me now? I glanced around to see if anybody else was listening, but they were watching for the bus, or standing listlessly, fanning themselves.

The mechanic squatted down beside the heavy chain and began to clean it with an oily cloth. 'It's a good thing because you have to have it in order to procreate. But it can also be misused. And that's how it can be bad.'

He paused. A young boy brought the mechanic a bottle of cola and waited while the man drank it.

'Yes, I see.' I felt uncomfortable, not knowing how to respond.

'Of course, he's quite right.'

'Yes,' I said again, as if I was perfectly familiar with what he was talking about. The mechanic handed the boy back the empty bottle.

A bus came, a double-decker tilting with the weight of people hanging on to the doorway. 'This is ours,' Dad said, tensing himself. I would have waited for another one, hoping it would be less crowded, but Dad loved this battle and fought his way on and I couldn't do anything else but follow behind. In the crush of bodies, I wondered if the whole journey had been planned around St Augustine, if it had been the run-up to it. This was what he wanted me to take away with me to be ready for Britain. Procreate, I thought. Yuk. The word make it seem rather disgusting.

We went down Chouringhee and around Dalhousie Square and along The Strand where huge pipes had been left for so long waiting to be laid under the road that refugees had made their homes in them. We passed a tea shop that had been set up by the side of the road under the shade of a tree, the man squatting behind a smoke-blackened dekchi of tea on a fire, and a long, rough bench where people sat to drink it. From between the bodies on the bus, I caught a glimpse of a woman's still, straight back as she sat drinking her tea, her long black plait hanging over her blue sari blouse.

I wanted to get off and drink tea like the woman was, but the bus roared past.

Once over Howrah bridge, Dad raised his heavy eyebrows at me, his grey eyes softened as if seeing me for the first time, and we pushed our way off.

India, by Design

Martin Goodman

'You're an aesthete…' Pete says.

The fabric stirs as he fingers the drapes of white silk that canopy my sleeping platform in my mountain cave in India.

'And ascetic,' he adds.

His finger, slick with saliva, trills across the bones of my rib cage.

He is bringing me back to earth. I already live in a cave, but this isn't what he means. He has stuck labels to things around my home, neat oblongs of white paper with words printed in blue letters. Lamp. Mat. Dry nettles. Ashes. Cave entrance. Satchel. Stool. Floor.

'Your turn,' he says.

We're playing a game. Using words to name things.

'Athlete,' I remember, and run my hand along the firm sinews of his left arm. 'Athletic.'

I stroke his hair. Even in the evening gloom I watch its blackness shine. I move my hand around to his face.

'Cheek,' I say.

It puts me in mind of a song somehow, so I hum it. It's a while before I come to the lines of the title, the words of association that started me off. I am humming a love song. Cole Porter's 'Cheek to Cheek'.

Pete's face shifts under my hand.

'Smile,' I declare.

He reaches up to my face, and finds that I am smiling too.

Pete slots a pair of Raybans over my eyes, takes me by the hand, and leads me outside.

He may not know it, my strength does not compare to his, but I am gripping his hand as hard as I can.

'This is dusk,' he tells me. 'The longer you look, the darker it will get.'

His words make sense. They are a lovely fiction. My eyes are like unexposed film. The longer I stand, the deeper the grey seems to burn. Suddenly my vision flares with light. Pete feels the shock in my body and leads me the few feet back to my home.

'It's the temple down below,' he explains. 'The strings of bulbs that line the towers lit up. Did they really seem so bright? They're very low wattage. Very dim.'

'Nothing is dim,' I tell him. 'Everything shines.'

'Arnie!' he says, almost whispering. He's learned to tread softly, even in happiness. 'You're talking. That was two sentences. A record.'

'I've been listening,' I tell him. 'All these months I've been listening. It's hard to talk while listening.'

'Listening to what?'

'Life,' I suppose. As I say it I know I can be more exact. 'The sound you make as you move through my days.'

'But I've not been here. I've been everywhere but here.'

'Your slipstream blows by and fills the cave. Come on. Light a candle behind me and sit on the bed. Now you're here, I can get used to brightness.'

He lights the candle, sits down, and takes off his shirt when I ask him to. I pick up the four medals he has brought back from his summer. Each hangs from a coloured ribbon and is gold. I loop them over his head. The colour of his skin is enough, the trim medallions of his nipples, but I take in the glint and dazzle from the metal on his chest as well.

'When you stood on the podium to collect each of these,' I tell him, 'and the anthem filled the stadium, do you know where it sounded the loudest? Here in this cave. The music echoed around the wall for weeks. As you raised your head I raised mine, and we looked up at the same flag stretched in the wind by your triumph. Which one is it? Which one is the Olympic gold?'

Pete lays his finger on one of the medals.

'It shone in this cave for several days after you won it, so there was never room for night.'

'But it was dark,' Pete says. 'I stood like you said, at the start of each event, and remembered to look in here. It was always dark.'

'So dark you couldn't see me?'

'No, never that dark.'

'You see!' I laugh. The laugh is high and wheezy and surprises me so much I laugh some more. 'There's no need to worry about me! Even when you're not here you light up my cave.'

I look around the cave during the night. The wall to the left of the opening shimmers like the sea. Sunlight catches on the tips of its waves. Pete sits at a table in front of it. He is in a harbour restaurant, and the waiter brings him a plate of food. Grilled sardines fan the rim of the white plate, like silver petals. Pete picks them up one by one, dips them in the sauce at the centre of the plate, and sucks the flesh from their miniature skeletons. Oil from the fish coats his lips. I turn from the vision to the man who sleeps beside me. I hear his breath as it brushes my skin.

This man is Pete. There's no doubt about it.

Which puts into question the man eating sardines.

When Pete opens his eyes in the morning, I am looking into them.

'Man of my dreams,' I tell him.

As a treat, I place an unused sprig of dried nettles into the bottom of my copper pot, fill it with water, and place it on the kerosene stove.

'When did you last eat freshly grilled sardines?' I ask, as we sip the tea.

'Never,' Pete says. 'I hate sardines. Just the smell as the lid peels back makes me want to throw up.'

These last few months visions of Pete have filled all of my days. I knew I was watching his life even as he lived it. Now that I've seen him eating in the harbour even as he slept beside me in the cave, I have to wonder.

And having wondered, I decide. My visions were not fantasies. They made me too happy for that. Those that have not yet happened will happen in the future. My visions were prophetic.

This way I have something to look forward to.

'One day you will eat fresh sardines. And love them,' I tell him.

And since we are talking prophecy, and we are in control of the future, I make a bit up.

'I'll reach forward and kiss the juice of the fish from your lips.'

Pete has ambitions for me. There is a hotel with a clean restaurant down in the town. He wants me to climb down from my mountain and eat a proper meal.

I'm prepared to try, since he wants it so much. It means becoming stronger.

As he boils me a meal of plain rice on the stove outdoors I pick up a pair of scissors. After ten minutes of vigorous exercise, one hand curled round each handle, I have the blades slicing nicely against each other.

Pete brought with him a parcel, wrapped in cheesecloth and tied with string. The string is sealed with wax so there is little chance of untying it. I bring the scissors to the task. The string frays, then splits, and I am able to pull the cheesecloth back.

The package is filled with material. Some squares are of cloth and others of silk. I spread them out and marvel at their colours before seeing the miracle of their patterning. There are two styles. One consists of geometrical shapes, largely triangles and diamonds. The joy is in their overlay. A range of colours, from dark to pale, allows a sense of looking into a distance or down into a depth. It is a perspective from on high of great and interlocking chains of mountain ranges. It is too glorious to look at for long so I bring my hands up to cover my face, then peep through my fingers for a fresh glimpse.

It is astonishing. In that single peep I recall the genesis of the whole pattern. Its lines are the lines of my fingers. Its triangles are the spaces where the light shines through from beyond.

I spread out an example of the other style of pattern.

The background is dark, in this instance dark purple. The outer rim is a thread of two bright colours, one green the other blue. And massed across the purple darkness is a maze of golden piping. Once I walked into a yard of sorghum harvest, balls of white cotton piled high against adobe walls. In the centre from a hook hung the unfleeced corpse of a sheep, whose entrails spiralled down to coil on the floor. The butcher, some years younger than me, opened his large brown eyes with surprise and gave me a gap-toothed smile. The sudden beauty of the scene had already shocked me into a smile of my own.

This memory is part of the design, but only part. Roots are there too, tendrils curling and spearing through the earth to sustain the leaves that stem from trees.

It is the sound that rumbles when I lay my head on Pete's stomach.

It is the beauty of all that stays hidden yet gives life.

Pete has left the rice to bubble, and is crouching in the cave opening as he watches me.

'They're yours,' he says. 'Designs from last winter.'

'They belong to winter.'

I pick up the scissors in one hand now, something has given me strength, and cut one strip from one of the pieces. It's a square of the triangles, the peep-fingered mountains, from deepest red to palest pink. When one strip is cut, I cut a second.

Pete is not alone now. The entrance of the cave is full, for a boy and girl stand beside him. The boy is perhaps five, the girl four. They come and visit whenever they have found anything beautiful. Today they place a cricket on the earth floor. It has a bright yellow chest and head, but its back and wings look waxed and black with a feathered pattern in bright white marked against it.

The creature stands still. The children walk around it when I beckon them closer. I tie one of the strips around the boy's head, as a bandanna, and the other in the girl's hair, as a ribbon. They both laugh lightly, turn, and scamper away.

'These scissors. My designs,' I say to Pete. 'These aren't idle gifts. You want me to work again?'

He shrugs his shoulders. He's against the light, so I can't see if he's smiling.

'It won't be like all this old stuff,' I warn him. I don't crumple up the stack of cloth in front of me. I can't be so rude with something so beautiful. But I manage to wave a dismissive hand at it. 'I don't have a pattern left in my head.'

'What is in your head?' Pete asks.

'You.'

My first walk from the cave takes me as far as a young mango tree. I have cut more strips from the collection of cloth, and tie some to the lowest branches. Pete takes the rest and climbs up the boughs, stretching his limbs and reaching out till the whole tree is festooned.

This wasn't my intention. But it's lovely to watch.

My second walk takes us back to the tree. Not a thread of material remains. This is perfect.

My third walk takes us further down the path, toward the town. There are a few shacks here. I sit beside Pete on a boulder and people walk the dirt tracks below us.

One boy, about fourteen, has two pieces of material tied together to hang as a sash around his chest. Like a beauty queen.

'This used to inspire me,' I tell Pete.

A woman flits between two houses. Three scraps of the new material have been stitched together, a colourful sling that cradles a baby against her breasts. Her hands support a bundle of firewood on her head.

'The signature of my designs, the defining stamp of an Arnold collection, were my openings for skin. I dressed my models with a tease of naked flesh. There's no tease to nudity here. It's what everyone has to show for themselves. The poor, the young and the lunatic go naked in the streets.'

An old man, his body erect, shuffles along a path from one shack to another. He is naked but for a scrap of white cloth tied around his waist and crotch like a diaper. His beard is long and yellow. His hair is tied back by a remnant of light blue silk.

'I bought bolts of cloth from the local market. Burnished gold, aquamarine blue and peacock green. Stretched them out on the hillside and asked for anyone who could draw on cloth to come to me. Seven people appeared. Two teenage boys, two teenage girls, two middle-aged women and an old man. Some drew patterns of elephants and monkeys and feathers. A woman filled a large section with fiery eyes. The old man brought a pallet of dies and stained a section of the golden cloth with fifteen colours, each stroke the size of a goldfish scale. This was fine but unexceptional. My creative life wasn't changed.

'I paid each of the artists, and made a gift to them of the fabric they had painted. All I asked was that they wear the fabric as they walked away. You've seen the results, Pete. They were the basis of my last collection. The girls and the women wound themselves in saris. One boy tied his cloth around his waist as a lunghi, what *Vogue* termed a revival of the male skirt. The old man simply flung his over his shoulder, the genesis of what *GQ* termed bathhouse fashion. The other teenage boy wound his into a cord around his sides, the material flaring into long flaps of material that hung between his legs both front and back. My own versions of the same design set the tone in St Tropez and Martinique the following summer. My career turned around. I had learned something. It wasn't the obvious lesson, the sheer casualness of the design. I learned from the way my artists put on their new clothes and carried them away. We use clothes to cover our bodies. For my artists their bodies were no embarrassment. They used clothes not as cover, but as adornment. Love your bodies. That's the lesson I learned. A designer succeeds with no effort when he starts from such perfection. Today I see things differently. We dressed a tree in the finest fabric. We came back to the tree stripped back to its branches, dressed in only its bark and leaves. Which was finer, Pete?'

He looks back at me, but when he sees my eyes are filled with tears he knows I have no need of an answer.

'I know nothing that adds to nature,' I say, and let the tears fall down my cheeks.

I am still twenty-eight as I climb back up the path to my cave, but feel very much older.

'Don't help me,' I snap, when Pete presses a hand in the small of my back to push me ahead. 'You run ahead.'

I watch him speed up the path, his trainers flashing white soles.

We used to be rivals in beauty, not so long ago.

It's time I did my body justice.

This is no place for Pete. And I have no place without him.

I shall let him take me back to Manhattan.

Steps lead down from the sidewalk. The place is another cave, but one of clean walls and subtle lighting. Reflections from the pool dapple the ceiling, shimmying in rhythm with the music that cascades from speakers.

'You've been here before,' I notice. Pete knows what to do. He slips his clothes into a locker, snaps the band with its key around his wrist, and drapes his towel over his shoulder.

'You're delicate,' he says. 'You need time to recover. We'll find new places together when you're strong again. For now this is perfect.'

I follow his example and undress. Men glance my way. Glances linger and catch my eye before going. It's more fascination than pity.

The walkway around the pool is columned, like a cloister. Some men walk around it but most are idle. They lean against the marble, or sit on the edge with their feet in the water. Few are single, though the pattern of couples and trios sometimes shift as men move.

I feel dizzy. Pete notices and curls an arm around my back.

'You're alright,' he says.

'It's the eyes,' I say. 'So many eyes. All this male energy swirling around the room. It caught me for a moment. Span me with it.'

We descend the steps into the pool. I float on my back, admiring the shimmering on the ceiling, then turn to find Pete's face beside me. His shoulders have dipped below the water. 'Please stand,' I say.

He does so. Water surges down him. His shoulders gleam. He is magnificent.

'Will you find us a room,' I say, and smile. 'I need to lie down.'

The rooms have no doors. I believe I sang. Something called to people. With Pete clasped between my legs I had looked at nothing else for a while. He surged like a dolphin breasting waves. We came together. I felt the warmth of him inside me, then held him close to the glue of my chest. It was then that I looked to the side. Three men watched from the door.

'We thought you'd break,' one said, and laughed.

I did break, I thought. And now I'm being mended.

Untouchable

Merryn Glover

There are two kinds of people in this world. Those that take life into their own hands, and those that have life taken from them. I am Laxmi, named for the goddess of beauty, love, wealth and luck. What more can you ask? From her four hands, lotus blossoms sprout and gold coins pour down. Today, my two hands are dirty from scrambling up a cliff, but in one fist I clutch a wad of rupee notes pulled from my father's body.

Yesterday two men came from the land office to measure out the fields around our village and record ownership. The measuring was simply done, and after that they spread out their books at Dal Ram's teashop to discuss the question of rightful possession. I slipped into the knot of people gathered around them. The men sat cross-legged on the string bed, leaning their backs against the wall, swatting idly at the sluggish flies. In the heat of the afternoon the thatched veranda gave ragged shade.

'There are two groups of people in this village,' said the long thin one, writing precise figures in his notebook. 'The Thakuris and the low caste.' Everyone pressed in to see: farmers, sweaty and smelling of earth, women carrying babies on their backs in fraying shawls, and wriggling children with chapped faces and dusty hair.

We are the low: *damai, kami, sarki,* the tailors, the ironmongers and the shoemakers. Because we work with the skin of the sacred cow, we are untouchable. The one blessing of these steep slopes is that cows slip and fall and die. That is when we move in. We skin the carcass and dry it for our leatherwork, boil the bones for glue and eat the flesh. We are reviled for it, but we eat the cow or starve. The Thakuris – who wear these sacred skins on their feet – are high caste and live in the top row of houses.

'Yes, two groups, and no doubt, they all have *claims* to the land.' The second man was short and fat and slurped his tea. 'But how can one be sure?' The people on the veranda shifted uneasily, squinted down at the mysterious marks in the record books.

The high-born Thakuris say they are descended from the kings of India. A Hindu prince escaped to these hills when the Mughals invaded Rajasthan. He built the first house on these steep slopes and all Thakuris are born of him. We do not believe this story, but we say nothing.

You see, there are two kinds of people in this world. Those that speak and those that are silent. Like my sister. Since the day she was born she has never uttered a word. Just grunts and moans and a strange hacking laugh when someone falls or hurts himself. Everyone calls her Lati, the name everyone uses for all born like her, the name everyone says with a finger twisting at the side of the head. Lati. Deaf. Dumb. Stupid.

At thirteen she was married off to a polio-bent man in the next village. They were a poor and filthy family and could get no better, so they accepted my sister. She worked hard for them and never fought off her husband. Twice she went to their cattle shed to deliver a child. Twice she laboured alone through the night, ripping the village cloak of silence with her screams. Twice she returned with a dead son in her arms.

When the *jankri* had finished purifying her in-laws' house after the second death, he told the family to be rid of her. She was bad luck, a vulture reborn, a witch. She heard his words from her straw mat outside the house and without sound, tightened the shawl between her bleeding legs and came home through the jungle.

When she got back here we had no food and she nearly died. But she somehow lived on air and words unspoken, words swallowed whole, till at last she grew fat and fatter still, and so fat that she burst and there was a rush of sound as her new baby daughter howled. And my father – who is one who speaks – swore and cursed and threatened to kill the father, to kill my sister, to kill the child. Instead he got drunk and lay in a pool of his own vomit on the veranda.

Lati lay in a pool of blood in the wind-blown cattle shed. Holding tight to her daughter, she refused to move till the child's mouth had clamped hard over her breast and suckled to sleep. Then only did Lati get up from the bloodied rags and straw and allow me to wash her. There was no knowing if this baby would speak or not, but in the weeks that followed she burbled and hummed and smiled so much I called her Asha, which means hope. Lati nodded. My mother shook her head and muttered that without even a father to name the child, what hope was there? My father at last looked down at the baby and invoked the gods to protect her.

Lest you forget, there are two kinds of people in this village. The high and the low. The high are pure and if touched by the low, will be polluted. Asha – bastard, female, daughter of a cow-eating idiot – is the lowest of the low. Untouchable. Lay a finger on her and you die.

I would sing to Asha when the smoke black of night filled our house.

Even though I was born from my mother's pure womb
I am forsaken.
The jankri has two hands and four rods
And I have more dark days than nights.
I have oil and a comb but my hair is wild
And I am forsaken.

I did not speak often, but I sang. I sang to my bees in their hive behind the house, and they gave me their finest honey. When there was enough I would walk the dusty path to Simikot, three hours away. On a good trip I could get a hundred rupees for a kilo. But I never told that to my parents. I always said it was only eighty, and I kept the rest tucked in a tight roll of cloth in the rafters. No one saw the two clever hands of Laxmi hoarding and hiding her tattered notes. It was for Asha, that she would one day go to school.

My mother used to speak out, but lost the will. Her voice became a mosquito whine, always hovering around the edges of you, until the moment of quiet – which was the worst – for that was when she bit. A sting across my mouth when I let a thought escape from the hive of my head. So I bit my thoughts and bent behind her as we cleared our narrow field.

'There are two kinds born into this world,' she sighed, crashing another rock into the heavy basket on her back. 'Men. And those better not born at all.' She harvested her stone, this hard-born, hard-bearing one and lamented.

A woman never knows a day of joy
The vulture drops a flower on the hill

A firefly catches the seed
A woman prays morning and night
She sows in sweat and reaps in tears.

Her losses were piled higher and heavier than the rocks on her back, but the ones she lamented most were her far away sons.

'There are two kinds of people in this village,' my brother said to me the night before he left, his sights on India. 'Those that leave, and those that stay here to rot.' That was five years ago and there has been no word since. But my mother places great faith in his return, like a prince on horseback, with saddlebags of silk, gold and cigarettes.

The next brother went to Nepalganj, and returned once. He said he was doing well, though didn't say what, and didn't bring anything. He squatted by the fire watching my mother cook, his filthy clothes reeking. A muscle twitched in his cheek as he followed her every move with glittering eyes. When the food was finally ready, he clutched his plate close to his mouth and ate, snarling and lip-smacking, till every bone was sucked clean.

Then he went with my father to Dal Ram's where the wily man pours out spirits for the numbing of pain. They set off together with arms around shoulders but returned shouting and pushing till one threw a punch and they lunged at each other, all teeth and spit like dogs. For his age and ailments my father was still fierce and with a blow from the tongs he overpowered his son. My brother ended up whimpering on a corner of the veranda, licking his sores. He left early the next day.

My father had a voice like his tools of trade: the bang and clatter of hammer against hot metal, the roar of furnace, the rasp of file. He spoke his mind, in all its crude waste; he knew whom he hated, whom he hurt, and whom he blamed.

His voice would scrape at Lati as he made exaggerated gestures, like speaking to a monkey.

'Lati!' Prodding her with a foot. 'I'm hungry. Get food.'

She always obeyed, her head low, eyes never meeting his. She was his chosen handmaiden because she was the only one who never spoke back, and never fought him off. When he commanded my mother she obeyed, but whined. When he tried it on me, I resisted, just as I resisted every marriage he tried to forge.

'Filthy witch! How dare you defy your father? Get out!'

The only voice my father loved was Asha's. He would pull her – now four and full of light – into his lap and chant to her, cackling at her soft echo.

99

The cock crows and we rise to work
In fields of desert where no rain falls.
Last year was drought, and if this year too
I will be broken, I will be broken.

Not Asha. She will not break against the rocks of these fields like all before her. I will see to that. My hands have been busy, wooing bees, harvesting honey and hiding the gains in my secret place. She is born for higher things, and my two hands will lift her there.

Meanwhile, my father's quivering hands are lifted sometimes to his ironwork, but more often to beating his family. Especially my mother. Over her he rakes all the coals of his bitterness. 'You are the cause of my ill-fortune! If only my parents had found me a lucky wife, a hard-working wife, an uncomplaining wife!'

But the fatal stroke of bad luck for my father came not from his wife, but from the pens of the land office men at Dal Ram's, cheerfully totting up their columns.

The thin man tapped his notebook. 'As government officials we must guarantee correct records.' There were nods and grunts. A woman shifted her water pot to the other hip and half smiled.

'Indeed, but it's a very tricky business,' said the fat one, shaking his head. 'I'm sure there are many disputes over ownership.' He ran his sharp eyes around the group. A farmer, dry and brown as a withered tree, stroked the handle of his plough, his forehead deeply lined.

'But, no matter, we will make sure the *rightful* owners go down in the records,' pronounced Thin Man. The girl at his elbow gazed up at him and sniffed hard at the two green trickles running down her upper lip.

'Oh, yes.' Fatso chimed, 'The *rightful* owners.' And with that he got to his feet and adjusted the *topi* on his head to a jaunty angle. A boy pounced on the pen left on the bed and was at once beneath a tackle of children.

The rightful owners of all the fields turned out to be the Thakuris. They even got their names down on the famished strips of land around the steepest side of the mountain: the fields that the low castes have always owned. Those mean fields no wider than a bullock and stacked one above the other like dirty plates; those dry fields that turn up more rock and dust than grain; those sunburnt fields where children in rags make small fires from the stalks and women labour, doubled-over in the barren soil.

The news of the lost fields ricocheted around the houses of the low.

'There are two kinds of people in this village,' my father blazed, working a glowing shard of iron into a scythe. 'Those that have and those that do not.' He pushed the piece into the red heat of his fire and turned it, his eyes like slits. 'And those that have, take everything from those without, and then still demand more.' He drew the blade out and lay it across his beating stone. 'The only thing they do not take is our debts. Those we keep till eternity.' With a large mallet he rained blows onto the shard, crushing and flattening it, his face slippery with sweat.

My mother sank down on the veranda, her head in her hands and set up a keening wail. Unable to bear it any longer, father threw down his mallet and went up to the Thakuris to beg for his field back. He returned at dusk, face a black heat. Going to the forge beside the house, he took a rod and prodded into the dead embers of the fire.

Lati sat at the end of the veranda with Asha in her lap. She was working her fingers through the girl's matted hair, pausing to pinch hard at nits, then pull them out and wipe them on her *lungi*. When father arrived she fell still and watched him, her hands resting on Asha's head. I too watched him, from the doorway of our house, the way you watch the sky before it splits open.

'What did they say?' asked mother, not lifting her head.

'They showed me papers. The records say it is theirs.'

'They know it is not!' she hissed. 'You cannot let them take it! We have nothing left!'

'What can I do?' father exploded. 'They have the money, they can bribe the men, they can read the records, they can say and do what they like and I can do nothing!'

'Nothing. That's right. You can do nothing, you useless, lazy drunk –'

Father hurled the rod at her, hitting her across the head and knocking her to the ground. There was a shriek and a jet of blood.

Everything happened all at once and was too fast and too slow. I fell upon my mother, blood spattering my face. The rod rolled down the veranda steps and across the path and on down the slope below our house, bouncing against rocks, banging and spinning as it fell. Lati fell upon my father, flailing at him with useless fists. Our neighbours' chicken took fright and sped flapping and squawking past our house. It ran over Lati, now face down on the ground. Asha stood on her corner of the veranda, clutching her hair and squealing as if a thousand nits had run wild across her scalp. Then I was upon my father and there was more blood on my face and I was yanked by my hair and thrown against the veranda. I hit a pile of iron scrap and it clattered and crashed until finally the last cooking pot rolled to a stop and all was quiet. My father was gone.

Night crept over our house. The bleeding on my mother's head finally stopped, and Lati and I dragged her inside and laid her on a mat. Her eyes opened and closed but she did not speak. At last Asha fell asleep on her mat in the corner, one hand snagged in her thorn bush hair. Lati lay beside her, an arm thrown across the child's back. Her wrist was scratched where a glass bangle had broken when she hit father. Her face was swollen and purple from his punch.

I stood up slowly, my head ringing. There was enough honey now for a trip to Simikot. We would go the next day and leave him. I moved to my secret place and pushed my hand into the space between the rafter and the thatch. I knew I had enough rupees for a few days until we found work. My fingers found dust. I scrabbled my hand around the rafters.

Nothing.

In the black jungle the fruit of the tree is black.
In the sky there is a sun and a moon,
But a black eagle also flies.
At the time of writing good luck,
I was with the eagle.
Either the luck writer was not true,
Or the pen has changed.

This morning his body was found down the mountain. Lati saw him first when she went out to fetch water. I came running because I heard a cry and a crash. When I got to her she was standing on the path, pointing and shaking. And there was that rasping laugh of hers. Her water pot lay shattered above my father's head. She was just laughing and pointing as if trying to say something at last.

The one blessing of these steep slopes is that men slip and fall and die. And the money – reeking of drink – was still warm in his pocket. Some gone, but enough left for Asha.

They say in these parts, that there are two kinds of people. Those born low and those born high. I say that there are those who fall lower than their birth, and those that rise above it.

Dowry

Usha Kishore

'Eighty gold sovereigns, ten lakh rupees and other accessories.'

'No, sixty sovereigns and six lakh rupees. Let's deal with the major issues, then discuss the other accessories! After all, our girl is a graduate, she will soon find a job.'

An hour of loud bargaining, coaxing and cajoling had led to: 'Right, let's settle for sixty-five sovereigns, seven lakh rupees plus the other accessories,' (which happened to be a motorbike, a fridge, a gas stove, a washing machine and other household appliances) and – 'Of course, the money for your daughter's winter outfits; they are very expensive and Delhi winters are terribly cold, you know! You are only giving all this for your daughter, we don't want a naya paisa for our son!'

This tasteless haggling between Rema's relatives and her cousin Kamakshi's prospective in-laws, after the 'viewing', had echoed and re-echoed in Rema's ears, for the past four years. Then, the argument had been vociferously punctuated by Kamakshi's tears. Now, the dowry haggling was happening in Rema's life.

Rema recalled the scenes of the old argument as she walked out of her house into the Indian summer. She had not eaten since the previous night. Heat was raining down with the morning light. It would soon be mid-day and impossible to walk on the road. Rema had forgotten her purse; she could not take a bus or hail one of the passing autorickshaws, which had the habit of slowing down for potential passengers. But where was she going? She did not even have an umbrella to shelter herself from the sun. However, the weather conditions did not bother Rema; she was far too preoccupied with the age-old tradition of arranged marriage. She had met a lot of suitable young men, while pursuing her various interests: some had fancied her, she had fancied some; but Rema had opted for the arranged marriage, within her own Brahmin community, as she had seen it work very well, around her.

Rema was just an ordinary girl in love with the ordinary things of life. To most of her relatives, she was a brat, born with a silver spoon in her mouth. Rema had a strong sense of the right and the wrong. She often stood up and opposed to anything unfair. In return, she was knighted: 'Brat!' That particular morning, Rema was staging yet another satyagraha, yet another crusade against dowry, one of India's social evils.

As she walked on, Rema re-lived the events of the past few days. A few weeks back, her aunt Gowri had brought this proposal, which was welcomed with delight by her mother, Saraswathi. The boy was not well-qualified, by Rema's standards. He had some sort of diploma from somewhere and worked at some firm in Thiruvananthapuram and was taking some engineering degree on some part-time course.

'You don't have to go far from home, then!' her mother had smiled.

'But, I want to marry a well-qualified person, I am a post-graduate, after all,' Rema had frowned. Above all, as part of the dowry, the boy's mother demanded a house, and that too the biggest of Rema's father's houses – because: 'You cannot maintain a household with one man's salary, and your girl is not working!' Rema had always wanted to marry someone, who would accept her for what she was; she did not want a gold-digger for a husband. Saraswathi had appeared worried, when Rema voiced her objections at the dinner table, which was a meeting point for the family. She had confronted Rema, 'All my friends' daughters are well-settled, most of them are well-educated like you. But, they don't behave like you. Do you know? My friends at the Mangalam Women's Club are blaming me for not getting you married off, for keeping you at home? They are also cautioning me against your umpteen chess tournaments.'

'Are they now? With friends like those…! Surely, they must be jealous of me, playing chess at national level.' Rema had risen to the bait. 'By the way, didn't you tell them that your daughter is a girl with strong principles and would rather die than pay a ransom to get married?'

'You don't understand. That is tradition!' Saraswathi had exploded. 'Oh,

God! Why did you give me such a daughter? Why can't she be like Gomathy Menon's sweet-tempered child or Sosamma Varghese's lovely girl? Why is it that only my daughter should be like this? What have I done to deserve this?' Streams of tears followed a hysterical sweep of hands that stretched heavenward.

'Really *Amma*! Try to understand my point. Can't you differentiate between tradition and social injustice? Why should I pay a house, a few hundred gold sovereigns, lakhs of rupees etc. etc. to get married to some under-qualified goon who thinks he is an engineer?'

Rema had caught her father's twinkling eye and her brother's smothered laugh across the dining table. 'You are the one who is spoiling this brat,' Saraswathi remarked to her husband, who was watching the drama unfold into a crisis with great amusement. Rema knew she was cornered; however, she tried another tactic: 'Now, let's debate on the issue of dowry – it is a mortal sin! Don't you know that dowry is illegal? Can I phone the police?'

'How many proposals have you refused, in the name of dowry?' Saraswathi had questioned in exasperation. Then, all of a sudden, she changed from hysterics to sugary sweetness, with the efficiency of a chameleon: 'Rema dear, you marry Srikanth and at least I can see you daily. You will only be living next door, in the big house. Srikanth is a good boy, very handsome. Apparently he met you during one of your chess tournaments. They want to come and see you tomorrow. His sister is the same age as you. She is a nice girl, you'll like her.'

Rema was furious. 'There is no point in me liking Srikanth's sister. I categorically refuse to marry that social parasite! Doesn't he have the backbone to save some money and buy his own house? And, who asked him to come and ogle at me, during my inter-state chess tournament? NO! Thank you! I will not pay a naya paisa in dowry! If somebody wants to marry me, he will have to accept me as I am. Does Srikanth want to marry me or does he want to marry the houses and property that *Appa* owns?

'I remember my friend, Rini's wedding: her in-laws demanded the legal rights to Rini's property, the previous day of the wedding. Do you know how frustrated Rini was? But, poor girl, she had to bow down to the wishes of her family. I am not like that. I prefer to be like Kusum *chechi*, who point-blank refused to marry the guy who demanded land and property the previous week of the wedding. She didn't care about the preparations or the hall or the reception or the guests. She is THE WOMAN!' Rema had stormed out of the dining room, before her mother could summon up another theatrical. Upstairs in her bedroom, Rema slumped on her bed and prayed to the huge painting of the dancing Shiva, 'Save Me! O Lord! Please!' Afterwards, frustrated and hungry, Rema had cried herself to sleep.

The next morning Rema washed, dressed and went downstairs, hoping against hope, that the incidents of the previous night would be forgotten. They were. She was greeted cordially by her mother, at the foot of the stairs, 'Come on quickly, my child, it's time for the morning pooja.'

Rema wondered: 'Is there a genuine change of mind? Is *Amma* trying to make up?'

Later at the dining table, Rema's questions were answered as Saraswathi teased her daughter, 'What sari are we wearing today then, and what jewellery?'

Rema gave her mother a questioning look.

'You know, Srikanth and his family are coming to see you today.'

'*Amma*, I thought I had made it clear that I am not at all happy.' Rema looked up from her hot cup of aromatic filter-coffee. They were having a late breakfast, that Sunday.

'Tough luck! They are coming this evening and you are going to say "Yes", OK!' Saraswathi sounded painfully decisive.

Rema stood up from the table. 'I am not marrying that spineless dowry-monger, who is after your biggest house!'

'So, it is the house that's worrying you, Rema?' *Appa* looked up from his plate of tasty *idlis*, spiced with chutney and chilly-mix, 'Saraswathi, if the girl doesn't want to marry that boy, let's look for someone more suitable. What about the bank officer then, Rema?'

'What? His parents just dropped in to view me as if I was cattle or something. They didn't even have the courtesy to let us know beforehand. I was exhibited before them and my musical talents, put to test. I was made to sing and play the veena and then the mother laid down her demands: hundred gold sovereigns, a pair of diamond studs, a house, a car and other accessories and the father was certainly keen on inspecting our houses and property. I totally disapprove of the parents and their demands. So, the bank officer is out!'

'She's on the shelf. She's twenty-five, now. All my friends' daughters of the same age are mothers. She'll never get married! Do you know? My sister Gowri and I went to Srikanth's house at least five times, before they agreed.' Saraswathi turned to her husband for help and receiving none from that quarter, continued, 'This girl's horoscope does not easily match with that of any boy. With great difficulty, we find a match and look what happens! Oh God! Why are you testing me in this way? Why was such a girl born to me?' She promptly burst into tears and Rema walked out, yet again.

'Another walkout, is it? You are well and truly cornered this time!' her brother Ramesh called out after Rema, with a mouthful of *idli*. Rema was not amused. She walked out of the room, out of the house, out of the gates and was on the road to nowhere. Rema's previous walkouts had resulted in her seeking asylum at her friend Shakthi's house. This time, she turned the corner, past Shakthi's house, past the bridge and walked out of Athani Lane. Rema kept walking. She glanced at the big clock-tower that stood vigil on the Vanchiyoor sub-courts. It was 11.30 a.m.

Rema was determined. She would rather die a maid than succumb to this dowry demon. She snapped out of her flashback and stopped at the Upudamoodu railway-bridge. She had not realised that she had walked this far. The summer sun beat down mercilessly and Rema was tired and hungry. Leaning on the railings of the bridge, Rema meditated on the railway track. She was oblivious of the roar of traffic behind her but fully aware of the funny looks of passers-by, who wondered what a lone young lady was doing at the bridge, in the heat of the mid-morning. 'No, I am not contemplating suicide,' Rema muttered, under her breath, 'I want to push all the dowry-mongers down, into the railway track, in front of the Parasuram Express; no, the Madras Mail would be better. And I hope the *Yakshi* who lives on the *Pala* tree would get them!' Rema laughed aloud and somewhere, a *bali-crow* echoed her laughter. Suddenly, she was jolted by the whirr of an autorickshaw. Rema turned around to find Gowri *chithi* stepping out of the three-wheeler:

'Rema, what are you doing here?'

'Standing.'

'Were you going somewhere?'

'No.'

'Then, what on earth are you standing here for, in that shabby *churidhar-kameez*, with your hair blown out by a Diwali fire-cracker?' Gowri *chithi* certainly shared her sister's flair for exageration and hysterics.

'I am thinking of pushing Srikanth and his family into the railway track, in front of the Parasuram.'

'You are in no mood for decent conversation. Come with me, this instant!'

'I am not going home!'

'OK, OK! We're going to my place.' Gowri instructed the autorickshaw driver. Before Rema could even bat an eyelid, she was bundled into the waiting autorickshaw, which did a U-turn in the middle of the road, holding up the traffic and totally ignoring the raised fists of other road-users.

'What, may I ask, is this tantrum for?' Gowri queried.

'I do not want to marry Srikanth!'

'Why?'

'His mother's demands. Didn't you tell them I am job-hunting? I am just between jobs. I will soon find a job. Now, they don't want to know all that. They are just after the house, that too, *Appa*'s biggest house. Their excuse is – 'the girl is unemployed.' Will they return the house, when I get a well paid job?'

'Who asked you to resign your previous job? It was a good one!' Gowri *chithi* promptly replied, 'Rema, you resigned because you could afford to! You have a rich family to fall back on!'

But Rema was not to be beaten. She retorted wryly, 'There was no room for self-expression in that job. Anyway, what are families for, then?'

'Coming back to the house issue,' Gowri *chithi* continued, 'Rema, don't be unreasonable. It is for you both. Not for anybody else. In this day and age, it is impossible to lead the life you are leading now, with one man's salary. You are so used to luxury.'

'I am happy to give up my lifestyle for a man who has principles and is anti-dowry.'

'Then why didn't you marry Shyamu – your *athai*'s sister-in-law's son? They didn't want any dowry and he is well-settled.'

'I can't stand him. He is so slimy!'

'Look, Rema, tell me frankly, do you have anyone else in mind?'

'Yes, I have a dozen in mind. Would you like a list?'

'Many people are wondering why you are not getting married. They think there is something wrong. We are all very worried. My poor sister is on the verge of a nervous breakdown. Can't you say "yes", at least for her sake?' Gowri *chithi* was now pleading with the irate girl.

'I am not getting married for anybody's sake. And, could you please tell the long line of people who are wondering about my prospective marriage that I do not believe in dowry.'

'Rema, I don't think Srikanth's family is asking a lot. Today, an engineer would easily get twenty lakhs and a doctor, thirty. It is a lot less in our Brahmin community. In other communities, they are asking fifty lakhs for an engineer and eighty to ninety for a doctor.'

'I am surprised, Gowri *chithi* that an educated lady like you should be speaking like this. Aren't you ashamed of yourself? What is India coming to – a bridegroom's market? Don't you know that dowry is a burning issue?'

'Are you punning?'

Ignoring the question and the underlying sarcasm, Rema proceeded with her argument, 'Don't you read daily in the newspapers about the bride-burnings, all in the name of dowry?'

'That is in North India. We are in the South. Such things do not happen here.'

'If we are not careful, the whole of India would become a bridal pyre, with the dowry demon dancing on top!' Rema was in her best 'social-reformer' mood.

'Who do you think you are? Raja Ram Mohun Roy? You know what? We have all spoilt you. You were a difficult child, a troublesome teenager and now, you have grown into an exasperating young lady!'

'*Touché*!'

'Stop at the Srikanteswaram Temple,' Gowri instructed the autorickshaw driver, who was choking with laughter at his passengers' conversation. 'We won't be long, please do wait.' Out of the driver's earshot, Gowri muttered, 'Isn't he ashamed of eavesdropping on other people's conversations?'

At the temple, Rema walked ahead. Her aunt bought an *archana* ticket at the little window and caught up with Rema, in the middle of her first pradakshinam. Rema stood in front of the giant banyan tree and closed her eyes. The squirrels on the tree were holding a chattering match, a cuckoo cooed from across the temple pond and the stone snake-gods at the foot of the tree were sound asleep. Rema looked around her – a temple official was sticking notices on the walls, announcing the forthcoming Sivarathri festival and an enlightened reader sat before the colossal, brass lamp, in front of the stone Nandi Bull and read the *Shiva Purana*, in a loud monotone.

'All's well with the world,' thought Rema, 'Why Me, O Lord?'

As if in answer to her thoughts, the temple bull walked past her, with great gusto; its bells and anklets tinkled into the sudden breeze that came as a welcome relief to Rema's burning face. She was woken up from her reverie by Gowri's hand on her shoulder, 'Come on, child, let's go!'

No reply.

'Rema!'

Still no reply.

'Come on, Rema!'

'I am praying!'

But Gowri was not in the listening mood and Rema found herself dragged into the inner temple, where she was greeted with the smell of oil-lamps, burning camphor and the pealing bells of *uchha pooja*. Aunt and niece stood before the dimly lit-altar with folded palms and watched the deeparadhana being performed. There were very few worshippers in front of the Sanctum Sanctorum. Gowri *chithi* drew her silk sari around her shoulders and prayed in earnest: '*Shambho, Mahadeva*! Grant sense to this child!'

Overcome with frustration, Rema appealed to the idol of the dancing Shiva: '*Shambho, Mahadeva*! Trample the *apasmara* demon of dowry and redeem the world!' Gowri could not hold back her chuckles. Rema studied her aunt, through the corners of her eyes. She saw the frown disappear and the taut features soften. Rema knew the signs. She was winning.

They soon finished their prayers and walked out of the giant temple gates and turned one last time at the golden flag-post and bowed their heads in supplication. In silence, a much calmer niece and a resigned aunt stepped into the waiting autorickshaw and were soon dropped off at the gates of Gowri's house.

On the verandah, Raju chithappa sat on his favourite rocking-chair, reading the *Indian Express*. His two young children played quietly in the shade of the pomegranate tree, ornamented by the entwining jasmine creeper. There was a languorous Sunday atmosphere to the whole house. Jasmine flowers had dropped down in the occasional breeze. They lit up the black, granite-paved drive like little white stars and decorated the elaborately coloured *Kolam* drawn in front of the house. The whole front yard was perfumed by the heady smell of jasmine. Rema walked into the coolness of the house. Raju folded his newspaper and greeted the grim-looking young lady, 'Hallo!'

Rema managed a weak smile and proceeded to the lounge. She slumped on a sofa. Gowri followed her niece, after having paid the autorickshaw-fare. Raju raised his eyebrows at his wife, as if questioning the silence of her usually chirpy niece. 'Rema has staged another walk-out!' Gowri muttered stoically.

'It's the Srikanth issue, isn't it? Gowri, why are you all forcing the poor child into something she does not like? The girl looks as if she has not eaten anything for days!' Raju came into the lounge. 'Rema, have you had any breakfast, my dear?'

'No, I haven't eaten, since last night.'

'Non-co-operation and fasting is it?' Raju guffawed. 'I must admit, Gowri, your niece is a true Gandhian!'

Without much further ado, Rema was led to the dining-area and plied with dosais, vadais and sambar. She quietly partook of the sumptuous feast. It was ambrosia after the previous night's fasting and the morning's missed breakfast. Raju chithappa sat down on a chair, next to Rema. 'Look, Rema, let's be reasonable! If you are anti-dowry, talk it through with your parents. Why stage walk-outs?'

Rema met her uncle's eyes, 'Because nobody understands…'

Glossary

'The Dowry' is set in the Tamil Brahmin Community in the South Indian State of Kerala. Originally hailing from the neighbouring State of Tamil Nadu; but settled in Kerala, the community speaks a dialect – a mixture of Tamil and Malayalam, the languages of both these states. Their traditions are also bi-cultural.

Naya paisa – New *paisa*. *Paisa* is Indian currency – an equivalent of a penny (not in value but in denomination.) The Indian Rupee is made of 100 paisa.

The viewing – In an Indian arranged marriage, the would-be bride is viewed by the prospective groom and his family. This is an elaborate ceremony.

One Lakh rupees – 100,000 rupees.

Sovereigns – Measurement of gold. One sovereign is approximately equal to nearly 350 grams.

Satyagraha – Translated as 'desire for truth'. It was Mahatma Gandhi's political warfare against the British Raj. The *satyagraha* is usually observed with a fast.

Thiruvananthapuram – Capital city of the South Indian state of Kerala.

Amma – Mother in Malayalam and Tamil.

Appa – Father in Tamil.

Chechi – Sister in Malayalam. Women older than oneself are referred to as *chechi*.

Pooja – Worship/prayers.

Shiva – One of the gods of the Hindu Trinity. Shiva is the dancing God.

Sari – Indian costume.

Idli – South Indian steam cakes.

Veena – South Indian string instrument.

Vanchiyoor, Upudamoodu – Places in Thiruvananthapuram.

Yakshi – Female spirit. It is believed that the *Yakshi* is the spirit of a wronged woman.

Pala tree – This is a tree with fragrant flowers. It is believed that during the flowering season, the tree is frequented by *Yakshis*, who are attracted to the fragrance.

Bali-crow – A kind of raven. Bali means 'death anniversary'. It is believed that the spirits of the deceased relatives appear during the anniversary ceremonies in the form of ravens, which are then fed.

Chithi – Tamil for aunt, usually mother's sister.

Churidhar kameez – Indian outfit.

Diwali – Indian festival of lights, celebrated with fire-works. Fire-cracker is another name for fire-work.

Athai – Tamil for father's sister.

Raja Ram Mohun Roy – Indian social reformer. Raja Ram Mohun Roy was responsible for abolishing the practice of sati, along with the British Governor General William Bentick. Sati was a practice where wives were burnt on the funeral pyre of their dead husbands.

Bride burning – In recent times, there have been many incidents of bride-burning, especially in North India. Young women who do not bring the requisite amount in dowry, are said to be burned alive by their in-laws and their deaths are usually passed off as accidents.

Archana – A special prayer performed by the priest. In order to avoid unnecessary delays, *archana* tickets are purchased at the temple office and handed to the priest at the Sanctum Sanctorum (inner temple). The priest then performs the prayers.

Pradakshinam – Going around the temple courtyard. This is a custom observed by Hindus.

Banyan Tree – Indian fig tree, considered sacred by the Hindus. Banyan Trees are usually planted in temple courtyards.

Sivarathri – Night of Shiva. This is a Hindu festival, celebrated in honour of Lord Shiva.

Nandi Bull – Lord Shiva's vehicle/mascot. The bull is sacred to Lord *Shiva*. Each *Shiva* temple in India, has a bull as a mascot, which usually wanders around the temple.

Shiva Purana – The epic of Lord Shiva.

Uchha pooja – Noon prayers.

Deeparadhana – the lighting of camphor. This signifies culmination of the Hindu worship.

Apasmara – The demon – embodiment of evil. Lord Shiva is portrayed as trampling the apasmara.

Shambho, Mahadeva! – Prayer – translated as Supplication to Mahadeva (Lord Shiva)

Chithappa – Tamil for uncle.

Flag Post or Kodimaram – This is seen in many Indian temples. The flag carries the insignia of the temple.

Kolam – A geometrical pattern drawn in front of Hindu houses. This is a Hindu tradition. The *Kolam* is highly elaborate and drawn using coloured powder.

Dosai – Pancake.

Vadai – Savoury doughnut.

Sambar – Thickened, spicy soup made of lentils and vegetables.

Naveen Kishore
Photographs: Kolkata

Sugarcane juice vendor getting ready for the day

Cinema hall advertising a Bengali film

FACING PAGE: Roadside barber; food vendor making beef, chicken and mutton rolls, a Calcutta speciality

Portrait of Mrinal Sen, renowned filmmaker

ABOVE: Asleep

BELOW: Boarding a bus at rush hour

Street children atop an abandoned car

Repairing a hand-pulled cart locally knows as a *thela*

Roadside food stall selling fresh *puris*

Shampa Ray

Hair

Wherever I went in that house, there was hair, long, often cooked hair. Every meal had at least one, in the rice, clearly, or in the main dish more obscurely. Perhaps it was wound around a chicken leg or submerged in the fibres of a cube of lamb, or just swimming on its own in the sauce. This last would find its way to its lodging house between back teeth. It was the only time in our house, that house, when we were allowed to complain at the table. 'Oh Ma,' we cried, 'Ma. Chool chool.' Then the offending hair would be teased out of the teeth, the rice, the sauce, off the plate or the spoon and held up as evidence. Then my mother would shake her head in a kind of forlorn recognition that some things were impossible, that there was no way she could control her hair loss, and she did have excess to begin with, and the weight of it gave her headaches when she was young, all of that in the resolute mouth of her as her hand flung today's hair-in-the-food into the bin.

No one got angry then. Hygiene was the great leveller in our family, the great obsessive compulsive disorder that kept real fear at bay. We were all hairy and we played with our hair long into the years when our mother was losing hers. But in those days it was thick and glossy.

Throwback

The blanket on my bed
The blanket under the sheet hung
        down the wallside
        in drips of emerald
The blanket twisted, striated by my
        sleeping
The blanket with the cream crocheted
        edge, a silent pocket
        of past
The blanket that isn't really a blanket
The blanket, in fact, was, but isn't,
        now just an undersheet
The blanket that's an excuse
The blanket that was warm in its own country
The blanket that belongs to me
I irreverently cuddle that blanket
        with my spine
        snatch it up in disgust or tears
The blanket that would have been for show
The blanket my grandmother made when
        she was twenty
The crochet that becomes looser than gravel
when I poke it with my toes
The blanket has a smell that is
Lake Road in the 1920s
The blanket my mother learned crochet from
The blanket, the green, the emerald,
the cotton, forgotten, under the white modern
sheet, with flaps of peeling bark,
resplendent in nature, just visible from
        under the bed
the blanket that is never, not ever
        on the floor

Hero

Years later I am there again
Noise and freedom rattle
from the bridge
I slump in the taxi
in a pool of hot plastic
sunk in the warmth of belonging
A spark in the terrible earth of time

The house, pink and crumbling
still draws me back
like a smile
There is no distance now
No difference, no pain or love
that is separate from this

Barefoot on terracotta and
a gate which is a grid. I run
Each step a prostration of joy
Everyone but me has moved on
No one but me cries for
the two-foot bed where
I curled up with you

No one looks for you
in the early morning lakewalk
Or longs to know the names of blossoms
No one stops to talk when I trail
our secret walk alone

The temple, once golden, is
saffron yellow, peeling
in anticipation of sudden sunset
It is drumming me home

There, I watch other children
Praying and asking for sweets
No beginning, no end, no place

I imagine you often
bringing you poems and
pictures I have done
You are by the brown lake
With two white flowers that
lie in your hand

Sudeep Sen

Prayer Call: Heat

I wake cold, I who
Prospered through dreams of heat
Wake to their residue,
Sweat, and a clinging sheet.
Thom Gunn, 'The Man with Night Sweats'

Outside, 'Allah-u-Akbar'
    pierces the dawn air —
It is still dark.

Inside, electric light
    powers strength
to my feverish body.

Mosque minaret
    radiate prayer-calls
all around —

like coded signals
    emanating
from old radio

transmitter-towers —
    relaying the dangers
of heat in this stale air.

≈

A bare body
    sleeps peacefully
beside me —

her face's innocence,
    and generous curve
of her eye

lashes, try to sweep
    away my
skin's excess heat,

one that is fast
    making my bones
pale and brittle.

≈

A brief lull
    lingers outside.
I cannot hear

the heavy lyrics,
    their rhymes
trying to invoke

peace and respect,
    their wafting baritone
instilling faith.

Such things
    are luxuries
for me now.

I lie, trying
 to piece together
the eccentric song

of my own
 inadequate breathing.
It is a struggle.

  ❧

It is also a mystery.
 Mystery of a body's
architecture,

its vulnerability,
 its efficient circulation —
they are perfect

models I remember
 from school's
very early lessons.

They are only
 how things ought to be,
not how they are.

  ❧

Only now, I realise
 the intent
of prayer's persuasion,

its seductive expression.
 I also value
the presence and grace

of the body that willingly
   lies next to me,
as her breath

tries to realign my will's
   magnetic imprint, and
my heart's irregular beat.

My vision is awash
   with salt
of her night-sweat.

My hearing is trapped
   within diaphragm's
circuitous drone —

in Arabic's passion
   that etches
its parabolic script,

sung loud
   so that no
slant or serif

can be erased,
   altered
or misunderstood.

     ↎

Religion's veil
   and chiffon —
its sheer black

and translucence,
   its own desire
to give and want,

its ambition
   to control
and preserve.

Such songs
   mean nothing
to me

if one's own
   peace and privacy
remain unprotected,

or, are not at ease.
   I want
the chant's passion,

its heat
   to settle
my restlessness.

I want the song
   to soothe
my nerve-ends

so that the pain
   subsides
and faith's will

enables to rise.
   I also want
the beauty

of this faith
   to raise
its heat —

not body-heat —
   but the heat
of healing.

    ❧

But for now,
   the diaphanous lull
is a big boon.

Here, I can calculate
   the exact path
of my body's

blood-flow,
   its unpredictable
rise and fall

of heat, and
   the way it infects
my imagination.

    ❧

I step out
   of the room's
warm safety.

I see
   the morning light
struggling

to gather muscle
   to remove
night's cataract.

    ❧

Again,
   the mosques threaten
to peel

their well-intentioned
   sounds —
to appease us all.

But I see
   only darkness,
and admire it —

I also admire
   the dignity and gravity
of heavy-water

and its blood —
   its peculiar
viscous fragility,

its own struggle
   to flow,
sculpt and resuscitate.

   ƫ

In quiet's privacy,
   I find
cold warmth

in my skin's
   permanent sweat,
in its acrid edge,

and in my own
   god's
prayer-call.

Translated from the Punjabi by Amritjit Singh and Judy Ray

Gurcharan Rampuri

Pens Coming Together

I
Waves converge to raise the storm.
All the blossoms spread their fragrance.

II
When the strings are touched, sleeping chords rise
with inspired harmonies to intoxicate the soul.

III
Atoms gather to fashion the universe
and drops of water collect to become the sea.

IV
Rays of the morning sun compose songs.
And when pens unite, they bring revolution to a time of history.

Recognition

I am the last soldier to die in the war,
O my enemy! my friend!

In the last minutes of battle
why did your dagger have to plunge into me
at the exact moment
I was dreaming of lying in bed.

Just wait and see –
Tomorrow these same leaders, your commanders and mine,
will sit together over drinks
They will smile
and divide among themselves the ground irrigated by our blood.

I am a guest now for a few minutes.
Be careful, don't set your foot
on a landmine hidden below
because that explosive
makes no distinction between 'us' and 'them'.

The Whip

I lived for years
under foreign skies
as if I was in my homeland.
I shared the same foods, language, and customs,
the same love, friends, and hunger.
Everything seemed familiar.

Suddenly, there came a moment
when a simple-minded man
lashed me with the whip of a racial slur.
I had been oblivious to reality.
Now I am part of the world that struggles against hate.

Shanta Acharya

Arranged Marriage

The bridegroom's profile
refracted through her purdah
of tears unused to the violence
of iconoclasm dressed as tradition.

That moment's reappraisal
warned her to faithlessness;
discard old ways for new,
worship new gods and shoes.

She was the arrow then
that darted forth from
the taut bow of culture into
the flaming pyre proclaiming

Impossible union with a stranger.
Love will rise like a phoenix, they said;
friendship will follow with the children of god.
But first one has to be turned inside out.

Ganesh Puja

A god sits alone
flushed in artificial neon lights,
red-blue-yellow-green chasing each other.

The fragrance of burnt out joss sticks,
incense and oil-lamp wicks mingle
with the smell of yesterday's flowers.
A god is left contemplating this world.

The puja ceremoniously done
the worshippers left, one by one.
Even the priest has retired to his daily chores.

I shall sit with you
lonely boy in the elephant trunk
recreating myths
that the years have forgotten to share with us.

I sit alone with a god alone
flushed in artificial neon lights,
red-blue-yellow-green chasing each other.

Fever in Diwali

Pious neighbours celebrated Diwali
with neat rows of oil lamps
promising the destruction of evil.

My fever flew fast through the coil of night
setting ablaze the desolate sky
like a child conspiring with confetti stars.

Harassed doctors came with tablets,
magic, miniature moons
with syrup in exorcist cups and hermetic brew.

While the snake-charmer's fluted thermometer
grinned its flinted fangs wider and wider,
I ate moons and laughed at stars.

My limbs could've even danced a few steps to appease
evil with the grace of lightning in a storm ripped sky
like blue throated Shiva with snakes in red matted hair.

White sheeted, I lay still
like an Indian monkey in summer.

Bus Ride to Char Minar

Cramped in a corner,
I ride a bus to Char Minar.
Bursting bodies press on me
as strangeness begs familiarity
in sharing a hard, narrow seat.

I feel the soft, wrinkled skin
of an old Hyderabadi begum
leaning to the window for fresh air,
gasping curses on Allah for her plight.

The mother with child at her breast
squats near my feet, quite content:
two little dirty hands tug innocently
the edge of my crumpled shawl.

Before I mingle again
in the crowd of Char Minar,
two sunken eyes offer me
eternity in a begging bowl,
promising me a reserved seat
in the crowded bus to heaven,
provided I pay the commission.

Jane Griffiths

Young Girl with a Flute
(circle of Vermeer)

I am uncertain, unattributable.
My face half shadowed by a saucer
hat, striped – the lilt of it.
One of my eyes, far away.

They call my right hand clumsy, say
the whole portrait, if it is one,
is like a large chest awkwardly
jammed across a door frame.

Light falls in diagonals, in a barricade.
Behind it, my flute rests against the table
while I talk to someone over your shoulder.
I have it loosely at my fingertips,
two of the stops just visible.
Don't we all need distraction, the hills?

Three Takes on a Location

Take 1

A stone's throw across the valley from
the town (steep terraces and an abandoned
campanile) there is the villa. Shuttered,

and nothing special, you say, just a stone
frieze of the moon and stars, a shell-
shaped basin. And a bridge

like an aquaduct marching on the first floor
entrance hall, and five people walking
round it, shaking stones from their shoes,

leaning and pointing across the balustrade.
The sun-crushed smell of bay. Under their feet,
the architect's imagination set in stone:

the arched, the orchestrated air.

Take 2

At the foot of the hills a ring
of tombs, Etruscan, cut from the stone.
Hollow as gaps in the memory.

We touch the altars, the alcoves.
What to make of them?

The farmer out among his beanstalks
with a broad-brimmed hat and
wheelbarrow is neither here nor there.

Take 3

Like a portrait without light behind the eyes,
three barred windows deep in the rockface.

The subterranean chapel of Mithras.
The chapel of the Virgin.

A priest raises his hands to the hill-
bearing columns, the traces of illumination:
St Christopher and Mary, repeatedly,

with dark-rimmed eyes, watching and fading.

The plaster on the floor.

And here we are walking above it all.

The avenue opens as if we'd been around before,
clutching awkward fistfuls of blackberries,

scuffing last year's leaves while the crickets
idiomatically turn over two disjointed notes.

Coda

Evening on the mountain: landfall made
visible in the ridgebacks of foliage:
the darks and darker stills.

The sky blue, the firs like pointers.
The sun setting in silver pintucks across the lake.
You could say it is raw material.

You could say it is.

Territorial

When the freeze came, we didn't think it strange.
It was the first winter in the new house, in
the new language. There were no known laws.

The small Renault driven out on the ice,
and the bonfire, were par for the course,
we thought; we saw straight through them

to the first house as it was with dark
glass set in white and knuckle-dusting walls,
before the burning. We learned to skate fast,

we saw the golden acrobatic fish frozen
under our dissecting blades, the triple-rimmed
eyes open, the stilled quiver of the scales.

We knew to spin in our own body's compass
and how to vanish, floodlit, in a crowd.
We had by heart the geometries of ice:

the smooth black cross-hatched, pockmarked
brown and frothy white. The gunmetal crack
when it would bear, and the other silence.

We were fluent as the wind until we heard
of drowning, found our pathways undulating
soft as ash along the quick-backed waves.

Naveen Kishore
Photographs: Durga Puja

A half-finished clay image of Kartik, son of Durga, who appears besides her with his brothers and sisters during the annual worship of the goddess in West Bengal

Fabricating a bamboo and cloth pavilion for the annual Durga Puja festival

FACING PAGE: A view of the half-finished demon king whose slaying by the goddess Durga is celebrated during the festival

A scene from the banks of the river Hooghly where hundreds of clay idols are immersed on the last night of the festival

FACING PAGE: An artisan putting final touches to his clay creations

Mahishasura, the demon king slain by Durga

FACING PAGE: The goddess Durga in all her finery

A stylised horse-like clay representation of Durga's mount, the Lion

Reviews

One Good Turn: A Jolly Murder Mystery
Kate Atkinson. Doubleday. ISBN 0385608008. £17.99

Be Near Me
Andrew O'Hagan. Faber. ISBN 0571216021. £16.99

Belonging
Ron Butlin. Serpent's Tail. ISBN 1852429151. £7.99

Those readers unsure about Kate Atkinson's involvement with crime writing, and who would prefer her to concentrate on what is termed 'literary fiction', really have nothing to fear. *One Good Turn* shows that whatever the genre, Atkinson is a consummately good writer. Neither a diversion, nor a piece of light entertainment, *One Good Turn* is a literary detective story, as solidly constructed as any of her previous novels, and with all the complexity and variety of the nineteenth-century English detective novel, in which enduring tradition Atkinson unmistakably writes.

In terms of technique, *One Good Turn* is absolutely traditional. Atkinson's ironic narrator makes the occasional intrusion, in the same way that the narrator does in Wilkie Collins. The story too is linear; it charts the inter-connected events of a few days during the Edinburgh Fringe, Tuesday through Friday. Nothing out of the ordinary at first, except for a commonplace occurrence of road-rage, then the murders, one on each of the four days.

Here is Edinburgh in high summer, where all of daily life is on show, and where the lives of the Fringe performance-goers are no more and no less bizarre than the performances they queue to see. With thirty or so characters, about half of them are active participants in the story; some, though, are already dead (and belong to the 'communion of saints', a realm that Atkinson does not ignore); a few are dying, or are to be dead; and some exist only within the novels within this novel – after all, this is Kate Atkinson. Gradually, we see how every character is connected, as does Jackson Brodie, who finds himself investigating the first of the murders, and begins to uncover 'boxes within boxes, dolls within dolls, worlds within worlds. Everything was connected. Everything in the whole world.'

A thoroughly jolly murder mystery, *One Good Turn* is also an Edinburgh novel in the Scottish tradition, that is, it is preoccupied with dualism: 'the Edinburgh disease, Jekyll and Hyde, dark and light, hill and valley, New Town, Old Town. Catholics and Protestants. A game of two halves. An eternal Manichean dichotomy.' As environment can help influence moral outlook, here all of Atkinson's characters display behaviour that comes with one or other of the divided aspects of this disease, and perhaps of the Scottish psyche. If there are to be more Jackson Brodie novels, then Atkinson will surely develop this theme. My suspicion is that we will see him again, for he has the makings of too interesting a creation to be consigned to cold oblivion.

Some may argue that there is no shortage of contemporary writers of Edinburgh crime fiction. But there is always room for one of Atkinson's ilk. In *One Good Turn*, she brings a version of *Bleak House* to the Edinburgh Fringe and gives an object lesson in how to make a jolly good murder story.

For a book that appeared on the 2006 Man Booker Prize longlist, Andrew O'Hagan's *Be Near Me* is surprisingly clunky. The main plot requires no great suspension of disbelief: some middle-aged Catholic priests and educators do fall in love with teenage boys. ('Erotic pedagogy' is a subject the Oxford classicist Mary Beard has recently found herself writing about in the press.) Some readers may find O'Hagan's subject-matter objectionable, but the story is neither improbable nor impossible and here, I suppose, my objections are more literary than moral. In O'Hagan's novel, there are devils in the details: implausibilities, inaccuracies, and simple errors that a good editor would have removed. Even if intended as instances of artistic licence, they bedevil the credibility of this novel.

A bad priest, like one of Graham Greene's 'whisky priests', and certainly foolish, Father David Anderton is not an especially bad man. More aesthete than ascetic, after twenty years 'spent in pastoral oblivion' in Blackpool he finds himself in a parish in Ayrshire. A half-Scot himself, David is a stranger in the land of his mother's forbears, and has come to a place where the 'Reformation had never stopped… with its briny dilution of Ireland's famous trouble.' Before long, the twin delights of sectarianism and Anglophobia, 'part of the national charm', are revealed to him. Both sides 'enslaved to the denominational impulse', all that flourishes now in Dalgarnock is bigotry and unemployment. As if art and beauty will be enough to save this aesthete from the barbarians, Father David creates a flower garden, and fills the church-house with beautiful things. One of these beautiful things is a fifteen-year-old ned, Mark McNulty, who 'behaved as if the world was invented just for him…

his face… convince[d] anyone who looked at him that things would be alright if one stuck close.' The priest does stick close to Mark, who introduces him to his ned-world of drink and drugs, thieving and petty crime. Loved-up one night on ecstasy tablets and drunk on vodka, Father David kisses the young man, and not sacramentally. Then he is charged with having committed a sexual assault on the schoolboy.

In a narrative that criss-crosses over fifty years, David's story is far from uncomplicated and is full of epiphanies. Aware that he is the 'sum of his failures', and acknowledging himself 'guilty, of something – of many things, perhaps, but not of what they say', he is anxious to tell the truth. There is no 'aesthetic defence' for his behaviour; and he knows that the time for believing in 'the miracles of art to help one to live one's life', as he did at school at Ampleforth, and at Oxford, is long over. On his journey towards self-knowledge he comes to learn that the Oxford that made him, also unmade him.

Fast-moving and told with great economy, *Belonging* extends and revitalises the traditional Gothic horror tale, telling the story of a couple hell-bent on a mutually destructive relationship.

Long before the full extent of the horrors that are to befall the couple becomes known, it is obvious that theirs is no conventional love-story. Jack and Anna have left Edinburgh to take up work as handyman and housekeeper in a luxury apartment complex in the French Alps. Anna is manipulative and destructive, Jack misogynistic and opportunist. No Babes in the Wood, they have both had difficult childhoods. Where Jack partly sublimates his troubled feelings, Anna celebrates hers. They are involved in a kind of *folie à deux*, with each being dependent on and feeding off the other's damage. Their relationship is unwholesome, and Jack recognises that 'something held us. Not love, but something more ruthless.' The *modus operandi* of their relationship consists of little more than 'the familiar craziness/forgiveness/megafuck cycle', which has become a kind of loving, and where 'the rough sex helped us – its violence passed for intimacy and affection.' High in the French Alps, they are drawn into someone else's tragedy. That on this visit to hell, they are innocent tourists is of no consequence: in the malign world they inhabit everyone is a victim, and everyone suffers. It is not a question of innocence or guilt.

Awaking to the seriousness of Anna's madness, and with the desire to be free of her, Jack's self-survival instinct takes over. Abandoning her at the Gare du Nord, just as they are about to travel back to Edinburgh, he flees in the opposite direction and hooks up with Thérèse, the French girl they met in the Alps, now living in Paris. What Jack regards as his comparative good fortune is only temporary: he finds himself back in the hellish embrace of Anna, who tracks him down to a remote corner of Spain, where he has gone to live with Thérèse. It never is entirely clear how Thérèse comes to be burned alive along with another man she has been sleeping with.

Belonging offers a deeply bleak picture of a malevolent world, where, Butlin reminds us, it is a terrible fate to be human, and part of the human condition for people, good or bad, to suffer.

Michael Lister

Shringara
Shanta Acharya. Shoestring Press. ISBN 190488623X. £8.95

'Shringara' is the business (or the time) of preparation. It's the getting-ready for something – in the case of the title poem, putting on make-up for, perhaps, an evening out. But it can also be seen as preparation for the business of daily life, or for the discovery of who we really are. The mirror, with its truths or falsehoods, plays its equivocal part in the process. Like many of Acharya's poems 'Shringara' begins simply, with the act of getting ready for the evening: but it opens out into the way our experiences, our acquaintances, lovers, family, those we meet and those we don't, are all part of the preparation of the person who in fact we are. 'A participant in life's carnival' she writes, 'I prefer the illusion... I travel towards what end I cannot say.' Chance and self-determination, the truth and illusion of the mirror each day define more exactly the self: 'this world, our ornament' is 'making us who we are'.

The notion and development of identity is a serious concern in this collection. Others include the shock of bereavement, as well as public disasters of one sort or another (New York's 9/11; the Orissa cyclone of 1999; London's 7 July; the anniversary of the Srebrenica massacre). Inevitably, given the title, there are poems about inherited traits and features ('Family Portrait'); there are poems inspired by painters dying young, as well as witty succinct poems, such as 'Almost' and 'Why?' There are moving and distinguished love-poems, to Acharya's grandfather (in four sections) and to her father (six sections): their loss lies behind the whole collection, and inspires its best work.

There's a constant tension between solitude and connection with others (again, defining the self). Interestingly these poems, often about love and loss – the threat of loneliness, telephoning home on Father's Day, the modifying effect of each passing moment – all display not narcissism but a characteristic generosity. Loneliness (that 'unfathomable continents of... loss') isn't being not loved by anyone – it's not having anyone to love. And there's a characteristic volte-face, too, at the end: loneliness is 'a secure place... an island of freedom and peace'.

Though focused on Acharya's own experience, there's a refreshing selflessness and detachment: no bitterness, no sentimentality, no self-indugence. 'Nothing's a gift', she stoutly says, 'not a breath can I claim to be my own'. Acharya's always at the face of life, never shirking hard lessons, trying to understand the purpose. She is never preachy, often entertaining. She's a grown-up poet, not afraid of seeming prosy in her simplicity: 'Learning', one of her best, combines complexity and simplicity in a dashing, flexible manner:

When we look at one object
we turn away from others.

To keep awake in the face
of such elision is to establish
an original relation with the universe.

I'm not in favour of abstract nouns in poems – but Acharya can usually get away with it. Her relaxed near-prosiness has developed over the years, and is a feature of her mature poetic voice. What may strike one initially as a kind of wordiness is in fact an attempt to say complex things simply and memorably, and sometimes this lends itself to a deliberately reflective movement. It's seldom, however, loose or slack, and there's plenty of evidence of her more formal skills in this as in other collections. (A rare achievement in a poet, Acharya can write with surprising precision and exactness about dreaming.)

There aren't any trivial subjects in Acharya's work. What I like about her writing is the unpretentiousness, the integrity, the direct struggle with language to make it speak truly about real concerns. Of course it doesn't always come off – inevitably there are passages that don't quite rise above floor-level, and a very occasional banality. *Shringara* is her strongest collection so far. Developing some of the concerns of *Looking In, Looking Out,* it shows the old wit ('Goodbye'), the old seriousness, the old honesty that are Acharya's trademarks, but it adds a new depth and confidence to her previous work.

R.V. Bailey

From Trocchi to Trainspotting: Scottish Critical Theory Since 1960
Michael Gardiner. Edinburgh University Press. ISBN 0748622330. £16.99

This book is premised on an interesting and original proposition. Gardiner argues the theoretical turn of French philosophy during the 1960s is a reaction against the foundational principles of the French Enlightenment. Against this model he asks us to consider Scotland. The birthplace of Hume, Smith and Robertson, Scotland is of primary importance to narratives of Enlightenment and the project of modernity. In view of such coincidence Gardiner asks, if post-war France produced Derrida, Foucault and Deleuze where are Scotland's critical theorists? *From Trocchi to Trainspotting* re-examines Scottish writing since the 1960s, both literary and critical, arguing that what has become known in academic circles as 'theory' has been happening in Scotland all along. Locating itself within the Scottish tradition of generalist education, the book draws on a variety of thinkers. Psychiatrist R.D. Laing and philosopher John Macmurray sit alongside contemporary critics such as Alan Riach and Pat Kane. These commentators are accompanied by artists and writers who exemplify for Gardiner an underestimated, but nonetheless real, theoretical turn within post-war Scottish thought – Muriel Spark, Alexander Trocchi, Edwin Morgan, Ian Hamilton Finlay and James Kelman. These writers are shown to express, and in many instances pre-date, ideas popularised by continental philosophers including Gilles Deleuze and Paul Virillio. Gardiner's book is an attempt to offer what is long overdue in Scottish criticism: a debate with international scope and one that is orientated toward the theoretical bent of contemporary literary studies.

Chapter One sets out the key concepts which inform the subsequent discussion of Scottish thought. Deleuze's doctoral thesis on Hume provides an important point of cultural contact. For Gardiner, confronting the legacy of Hume has been just as important for Scots as Rousseau has been for a generation of French thinkers. Robert Crawford's argument that the Scottish Enlightenment invented the concept of English Literature is a key adjunct to Gardiner's analysis. It allows him to argue that the epistemological uncertainty, the radical aesthetics and de-territorialising tendency of recent Scottish writing belongs to an assertion of Scottish cultural independence. Many critics have argued that the post-79 era signals a second, and often more real, renaissance within Scottish Literature. Gardiner challenges this chronology and looks to trace how these narratives of discontent have been fermenting long before Kelman, Gray et al came to prominence in the 1980s. This is an astute point and acknowledges the fact that *Lanark* (1981) was three decades in the making. The postmodern self-awareness of Gray's landmark novel owes much to the technique of Muriel Spark, writing in the late 1950s. For Gardiner, Spark's work belongs to a literary auld alliance with French writer Alain Robbe-Grillet and the *nouveau roman*. Chapter Three focuses on Spark's first three novels, *The Comforters* (1957), *Momento Mori* (1959) and *The Ballad of Peckham Rye* (1960). Gardiner argues that the formal innovations of Spark's fiction should be read not as the work of the classic ex-pat author but in terms of a specifically Scottish upbringing in the capital city of the Enlightenment, Edinburgh. Chapter Four focuses on the work of Alexander Trocchi and his links with Guy Debord and the French Situationists in the 1950s. Gardiner uses Trocchi and Situationism to argue that that the recent devolutionary changes within Scotland are part of a culture-led programme of reform. The book performs the important task of re-examining Trocchi's work as founder and editor of the avant-garde literary magazine *Merlin* (1952–54). *Merlin* was important in bringing writers like Beckett and Sartre to the attention of English-speaking readers. Chapter Five concentrates on Edwin Morgan, specifically *Emergent Poems* (1967), *The Second Life* (1968), *Glasgow Sonnets* (1972), *Sonnets from Scotland* (1984) and *Newspoems* (1987). Morgan's concrete poetry is argued as disrupting the canonical tendencies of traditional Eng. Lit. by rendering the conventions of prosody inherently problematic. Gardiner argues that the author is a DJ who creates new meanings and patterns by mixing and scratching across the surface of our contemporary cultural sedimentation. Chapter Six focuses on Ian Hamilton Finlay, while Chapter Seven examines James Kelman's non-fiction, including his writings on Glasgow as the City of Culture 1990, Chomsky and the Scottish tradition of common sense, and the narrative techniques of Kafka. The chapter ends with a Deleuzian reading of Kelman's Booker Prize winning novel *How Late It Was, How Late* (1994).

From Trocchi to Trainspotting is an important and bold attempt to push the boundaries of contemporary Scottish Studies. In one of his most insightful and lasting images, Gardiner juxtaposes the logic of Enlightenment Edinburgh's New Town with the principles of ordered planning that underpinned the creation of housing schemes during the 1960s. The book attempts an archaeology of a key period of Scottish writing, one that has so far remained relatively unexamined. Admittedly, on occasion the theoretical acrobatics of the analysis become a little dizzying. However, Gardiner's work continues to ask a series of questions that are original and deeply provocative.

Matthew McGuire

This Life, This Life: New and Selected Poems, 1970–2006
Andrew Greig. Bloodaxe Books. ISBN 1852247134. £10.95

Compiling a volume of 'new and selected poems' has always seemed to me to be an oddly treacherous endeavour: as when sitting down to reminisce with an old school-friend, it is inevitable that, among the highlights of days-gone-by, you will revisit some awkward moment from the past as well. To a certain degree, Andrew Greig's *This Life, This Life: New and Selected Poems 1970–2006* has confirmed what I had suspected of such a collection, though I've been reminded, too, of the joys inherent in sharing in a retrospective such as this.

Greig's early poems, while not without merit in their own right, can be said to contain some 'awkward moments' when compared to his more refined, later works. For example, in 'On Falling', from his second collection, *Men on Ice*, the poet writes, 'You'll be sure and fall *in*/and you'll take deep rest/in your deep-ression/when you fall as we all/do right down some terrible night.' These lines show a tendency towards punning, and the extent to which rhythm often drove his lines, a fact which contributed to hard internal or end rhyming and, in this case, a jarring line-break.

A retrospective collection offers the opportunity to re-examine half a life's body of work in terms of its later self. Given distance and hindsight, we're able to comprehend the artist's poetic development over a significant period of time, and in this regard *This Life, This Life* illustrates the development of Greig's style from collection to collection.

In *Surviving Passages*, published five years after *Men on Ice*, we can see evolution towards a more nuanced sense of rhythm, enjambment and word usage, as in these lines from 'In the Tool-Shed': 'They come in clutches; azaleas, zebras, zambesi./Orchids, oranges, oran-utangs hang/from their common mouth.' The poet weaves from narrative into voluptuous listing without falling into a stultifying rhythm. Similarly, in *Surviving Passages* and subsequent volumes, we witness a shift in the ways that Greig's favoured themes – love, mortality and personal awareness – are presented, from the outright declaration of an idea to its careful treatment through demonstration.

Greig's most recent poems – those from *Into You*, along with the new poems of this volume – are a kind of maturity-made-manifest; the visible culmination of three and a half decades of poetic development, undoubtedly representing his finest work to date. Take, for example, the austerity and confidence of a poem such as 'Vow', in which Greig instructs his reader to take 'the bowl that's always brimming./Bear it carefully through this world./

Let nothing spill./Let there be no tears, not a drop.' Here the poet has truly mastered the economy of the line and its music, the once-pounding rhythms refined and employed in the artful way that the lines' varied lengths carry the reader along. Likewise, a number of recent narrative poems illustrate anew the relationships of men, women and families, the elusiveness of history and memory, the foreknowledge of mortality, and several of the other themes that Greig has returned to time and again. Greig's narrative poems move with the same assurance and subtlety as his lyrics by acting situationally instead of discursively. All of his poems move to considerable effect.

This Life, This Life has confirmed for me the double-edged nature of compiling and publishing a collection of new and selected poems. It is certainly unfair that we retroactively measure an artist's early poems against his most recent work, but we do. Irregardless, it is a gem for what it reveals of this accomplished poet's constant and fastidious refinement of style.

Stephen Lackaye

There Are Words: Collected Poems
Gael Turnbull. Shearsman. ISBN 0907562892. £18.95

To read Gael Turnbull's collected poems is to experience a sense of a life lived, and lived to the full. Turnbull was both poet and doctor (like William Carlos Williams, whose work he admired) who practised in Canada, America and in the UK, and eventually settled in Edinburgh, his birthplace, with his wife, Jill. He was also a sailor, mountaineer and Morris-dancer, and it is not too fanciful to say that I find an energy and lightness of foot in his poetry, and something akin to dance in his use of syntax. The founder of Migrant Press, he introduced the work of many transatlantic poets to British readers, and he had a deep knowledge and appreciation of French poetry. He also created strikingly original poem-machines that unfolded, spun, or changed shape, and delighted audiences everywhere.

Here is an astonishing range of form and subject, rhymed and unrhymed, from one-word lines to the long line, sonnets and villanelles, 'found' poems and prose-poems, political declarations and declarations of love. Turnbull is a poet who was always experimenting with fresh ways of saying, examining the relationship between the words on the page and the spaces around words. The voice is unmistakable: questioning, qualifying, doubling back on itself, then leaping forward, always on the move, dancing. Here, for example, in 'VI' from

Twenty Words, Twenty Days (1966) he examines the atmosphere in the wake of Kennedy's assassination:

> a nausea in the air as of
>> some sort of gas leaking –
>>> and implying…no, more than that…
> insisting upon a realisation of our
>> UNDERVALUATION
>>> of all that
> 'other', that unbelievable and extraneous, that fairy-tale of king's
> daughters and wicked magicians that is history –
>>> now grubby with
> detail –
> smeared on the seat of a car, soaked into the pleats of a
> skirt –

The questioning overview, gathering-in precision and the detached close-up are typical of this fine diagnostician of the world's grief, whose affectionate voice convinces us that he suffers alongside the patient. Indeed, his deeply-moving, elegiac poem, 'Impellings' (*For Whose Delight*, 1996), has the freshness of case-notes. In it, he embraces other lives, celebrating, mourning, remembering, and weaving them together.

The sense of life as something to be held, relished and yet humbly surrendered, is essential to Turnbull's writing, and it informs the whole of *Transmutations* (1997), where, for example, the scent of burning juniper on the fire evokes:

> the presence of a time not now and a place not here
> so immediate that it's as if the answer to some first and final question
> had been revealed and was to be found only in what is lost at every
> moment.

He sees things in the round and, frequently, the perspective is unforeseen and paradoxical, as when, at dawn, 'lappings of day' reveal:

> …mud flats of the night exposed where we may venture,
> fearful perhaps but curious to find what the glare of too much light
> may have concealed.

Fiercely ironic in denouncing injustice – see 'The Ballad of Rillington Place' – lyrical and concise, Turnbull is preternaturally attentive to nuance and ambiguity, never more so than in the devastating five lines of 'On the Somme':

'Nothing was spared'
  said the guide
'and no one needed
the full cost
of this monument.'

At every turn he is preoccupied with 'foraging for it, that word', as in 'Something So Singular', where the poet celebrates 'whatever it is that is ours/ unimaginable to others'. Turnbull's love of singularity has given us poems like 'The Slater' (as in 'woodlouse'), 'A Racing Walker', and 'All the Blue: From the Director's Book of Josiah Spode', a 'found' poem to relish for its eighteenth-century precision.

These are poems of high specific gravity, dense with meaning, sometimes resembling the beginnings of short stories, so deftly does Turnbull catch the tone of a voice, a gesture, a quality of the light; poems whose reverberations suddenly strike the heart and make you weep. *There are Words* challenges us to search for those mysterious presences, words, now lost:

for a particular size of stone about the size of your fist
for water only just enough to cover something
for little walks which an invalid could be expected to take

or even 'for the indulgence of finding words'.

Anna Crowe

Or the Day Seizes You
Rajorshi Chakraborti. Penguin Books (India). ISBN 0144000563. Rs 250

Rajorshi Chakraborti's intriguing debut inverts the phrase *carpe diem* as its philosophical starting point. If Horace exhorts in *Odes* 1.11 that we must seize the day because time is fleeing, Chakraborti portrays humans on the run because time has become meaningless. His style owes something to surrealism, his content to Kafka. Although the prologue begins with his protagonist's childhood, it is leitmotifs as much as narrative that give the book structure. *Or the Day Seizes You* can be a disjointed read, but it is novel of ideas that, once lodged in a reader's mind, will firmly stay there. It is a nice touch that the cover design includes details from two Dali paintings, *The Persistence of Memory* and *Sleep*, which features a dozing head lashed to the ground, whilst the foreground shows pristine white shirts and T-shirts.

Chakraborti's protagonist Niladri Dasgupta is a thirty-something business-man and father who is a perfect white shirt candidate. Despite marriage, a child and divorce, he is almost a blank slate. The plot charts five years in his life, starting from an incident where a complaint about his daughter's behaviour leads him to discover his wife's adultery. He goes into self-imposed exile in London, returning to India only for his murdered uncle's funeral. There he discovers the truth about family feuds, and meets his daughter and ex-wife. Before events can settle down, his family must leave Calcutta because his father has antagonised the local warlord. They arrive in Bombay just in time for the '7th December' atrocities amid a growing climate of fear. Vignettes of Niladri's London life are inserted into the story, including ill-fated trips to an enormous brothel, and to Normandy.

Condensed, this sounds exciting, but having Niladri as a first person narrator ensures that a reader is only allowed grains of understanding. Niladri's father says to him there's a lot in people you don't know, something you never seem to notice.' The sub-text also suggests that there's not a lot in Niladri for other people to notice. But if he is 'nothing' – and Chakraborti chooses an opening quotation from V.S. Naipaul on this theme – then, the book suggests, it is the result of society. Niladri's identity has been contingent on ready-made roles, but when these start to disappear, his whole identity melts in a similar manner to Dali's clocks.

So far so surrealist, but it would be a mistake to take the connection too far. Broadly speaking, the surrealists wanted to free people from what the movement saw as false rationality and restrictive customs. 'Beauty will be convulsive or not at all,' declared André Breton. Not that there is much beauty in Chakraborti's novel. And even as Niladri tries to recreate himself in a rapidly shattering world, you aren't sure he really achieves anything. He spends most of the book running away, with his daughter Shormila when he learns of his wife's unfaithfulness, then to London, back to Calcutta, then to Bombay and finally to Pune, a destination he picks at random.

Niladri is a man in the grip of events who has lost control, or perhaps taking control simply isn't possible. There is an interesting rant in the second to last chapter by Debu, an intellectual, about his vision for a book. It must capture a world 'as shamelessly full as ever – apathetic, incongruous, obscenely simultaneous'. In this environment, locating yourself in the centre is impossible, pretending your view of the world 'makes sense', close to madness. The division between dream lives and 'real' lives is precarious and sometimes non-existent. Niladri spends the best part of five years thinking he had a relationship with his ex-wife; that it isn't really over. When he visits her after his uncle's murder, she has incontrovertibly moved on, with a new baby as well as husband.

In Niladri's London room 'the clocks actually slowed down', and he doesn't seem to be speaking metaphorically because he tests them to be certain. The novel is filled with such instances of dislocation, of an inability for anything to run from start to finish. Instead Chakraborti inserts recurring leitmotifs, including huge bridges and slippery slopes. Both are connected with drama, either physical or emotional (the two rolling effortlessly into one another), reasserting the idea that connection – the purpose of a bridge or slope – is a hazardous and unpredictable affair. Emotional connection is equally difficult and the main male characters spend a disproportionate amount of time thinking about absent women. The women in question, ex-wives, lovers or prostitutes, are viewed in an explicit, voyeuristic manner.

Given the novel's preference for the abstract, the long rants about destructive Western capitalism and immigration are quite hard to fathom. Characters as diverse as Gombrowicz, Niladri's Polish friend and a Nigerian whom they meet at the brothel, go on at some length. Possibly, it is less the content than the impassioned, one-sided rhetoric of the diatribes, which interests Chakraborti. His protagonist shouts at his cousin that 'your fuckin ideas are just for you', before running for the final time. It is a hard idea to stomach in these personality-heavy times, but Chakraborti seems to suggest that it is only through the prism of an absent identity that the world can accurately be described. This might not make easy reading, but for originality it's hard to beat.

Hannah Adcock

Rain
Sudeep Sen. HB. Gallerie/MapinLit. ISBN 8190199900. £19.95

Rain is a new realisation of Sudeep Sen's 2002 project originally published in India under the title *Monsoon*. A difficult book to pin down to any genre, the twenty-two selections include a haiku and a concrete poem, all typified by an intelligent, reflective brand of prose that verges on poetry. Paired as the writing is with the works of contemporary Indian artists, the resulting volume is physically very beautiful. For the meticulous Sen, structure and presentation are important, as can be seen in his previous volumes, *Prayer Flag* and *Distracted Geographies: An Archipelago of Intent*.

Not only does the selected artwork in *Rain* show his keen sense of the visual counterpoint desired for his work, but the words themselves are also carefully arrayed on the page. Indeed, in the two octets, the reader is deluged with rhythmic monsoon-like downpours of writing, which in the closing sestet reduce to short, stacatto bursts. The words are twinned to this structural purpose; even the quotations selected to introduce the sestet do not mention rain, but rather are about need, and seduction.

While the first of the six pieces in this final section expresses Sen's struggle to 'emerge out of this heavy, rain-filled air' of the earlier octets, the book culminates with the author's confession in 'Knowledge, Need' that escape is not his true desire:

'The more you know, the less you
need'—but that is not true at all for
thirst, water, or rain.

Rain is an ambitious, highly personal artistic endeavour, and is largely a success. In 'Offering, Fluids' – clearly a favorite of the author, as it also appears in slightly varied format in the two above-mentioned collections – Sen is at his best. The language is precise and taut, creating in its rhythms the desire and tension conveyed by the words, and encapsulating the intense passion which is characteristic of the book, and Sen's work in general:

There are no endings here—only beginnings—precious incipience—translucent drops
of sweat perched precariously on her collar-
bone, waiting to slide, roll unannounced into
the gulleys that yearn to soak in the rain—

Due to the personal and elemental nature of this volume, the language is often impressionistic. Although the overall impact is convincing, there are passages in the octets where the force of *Rain* is somewhat weakened by prose which has a decidedly scientific feel to it. Indeed, as the author says himself, 'Somehow technological similes used to compare elements in nature are always fraught with dubious results.' Rain, though, is an uneven and unpredictable phenomenon, after all. Sudeep Sen's *Rain* ebbs and flows, but on balance, the strengths of the work far outweigh the weaknesses. An enjoyable journey, and the final confession of thirst – for more of the same – rings true.

Andy Gloege

The Cleaner Fish
Gordon Meade. Arrowhead. ISBN 1904852106. £7.50

Protagoras claimed that 'man is the measure of all things: of what is, that it is; of what is not, that it is not'. Aristotle described man as being a 'communal animal'. And Socrates defined humans as 'featherless bipeds'. Man's identity lies in measurement, more specifically, the need to compare likeness with or dissimilarity from another living being. The search for identity is a constant state of self-reflection, and poetry has always been a vehicle to consider the notion of 'oneself'.

The Cleaner Fish is a lovely and considered collection of poems, packed with quiet insights into the private lives of birds, reptiles, and sea-life. In the first section, it is as though Meade has gone bird-watching and whispers thoughtful observations in his reader's ear, 'the song of the chough/is little more than a cough;/the nervous sort a poet might give before he starts to read from his latest work,' or standing in the Florida mangroves, each egret, 'will return to outshine/the morning sun; each one a lighthouse beam/of feathers; a snowflake of muscle and bone.' This attention to precision and grace existing in the natural world is reminiscent of haiku images, and can be seen throughout the collection.

'The Shark' is perhaps the most successful of the nature poems. Meade begins by admiring the shark's 'non-thinking, totally instinctual,/predatory gifts,' the ability 'to get rid of all one's/psycho-babble, the white noise/of the human species, and just exist.' The tone shifts from admiration to envy at being blissfully uninformed. Meade wishes to know nothing of Freud, Jung, or Melanie Klein, and yet he cannot help expressing this desire in psychological terms. The poem reaches the height of self-consciousness during a lesson on the instincts of art, 'to offload Shakespeare and unplug Bach; to have/ never seen a Rembrandt, nor a Monet,/nor a Braque. To be one's own work /of art, a one-man show, a performance piece, a word-/less monologue of cartilage and teeth.' When he compares his work to the great masters', he once again becomes jealous of the shark's freedom, and suggests that sapience has complicated man, rather than making him a superior being.

Meade's nature poems are juxtaposed with reflections on familial relationships, particularly in regard to his mother as a negative component. In 'The Duckbill Platypus', he turns to his parents as a source of self-discovery: 'I am told I have/my mother's veins,/but through them/runs my father's blood.' It appears that he attempts to cancel out characteristics inherited from his mother, with traits of his father he deems as 'good': 'I am told I have/my mother's heart,/but it is fuelled by my father's love.' At the end of the poem he discovers that his identity does not have to be determined by other people, 'and down there/in the darkness/in the silence,/in the cold,/all that matters/ are my feelings,/and not what/I've been told.'

The Cleaner Fish is much more than a trip to Deep Sea World. It is a remarkable collection dealing with the complexities of human understanding, awareness of the environment, and how we identify ourselves in regard to one another. Meade dares to expose our shortcomings, 'the unnatural greyness of man', using a cause-and-effect logic. More specifically, he depicts the outcome of human action on the animal kingdom and, through subtle images rather than through propaganda, suggests that man is perhaps the inferior being.

Lauren Pope

Surface
Siddhartha Deb. Picador. ISBN 0330489240. £7.99

Siddhartha Deb's second novel is, at least superficially, a political thriller. The novel's protagonist Amrit Singh is a minor journalist for the *Sentinel*, a decaying Calcutta newspaper. It is the early 1990s and the somewhat lethargic Amrit is required by his editor to travel to a remote part of north-east India on the fringes of the Burmese border, a location 'forgotten by the world'. Whilst researching the area, Amrit discovers a photograph of a young woman flanked by two armed terrorists. The writing on the back declares she was subsequently executed for making a pornographic film. Fascinated by this, Amrit feels that his journey will allow him to investigate the story, thereby improving his employment prospects. Both literally and metaphorically, the photograph is 'a window to a distant place'. Amrit's friend, a German correspondent, secures him a commission to produce 'a portrait of the mystery and sorrow of India through the story of the woman in the photograph'. In the course of his somewhat laconic pursuit of information, Amrit learns of the Prosperity Project, an 'alternative community' run by the visionary Malik, 'a creator of order in the wilderness'. Increasingly, this community becomes the focus of his investigation.

Issues of identity, personal and national, are a central concern of the novel. On his journey, Amrit meets many 'strangers with a desperate edge to their stories' and these tales compose much of the narrative. His journey is slow, beset by obstacles he seems in no hurry to overcome. The novel's dramas are acted out on the margins of a republic where borders are fluid and contested. The characters, too, are peripheral: retired, in menial posts, or the wives of great men. Their stories are vignettes, Amrit notes, a 'partial, incomplete account'. The languid pace and unresolved narratives may disconcert those in search of a swiftly-moving thriller. For in many ways, the real pursuit is Amrit's search for himself. Malik, too, lacks a sense of self, believing he can create reality from illusion. He is aware that 'the power of image' is underestimated and the Prosperity Project only ever existed as a series of staged photographs, 'like a sequence of surfaces without depth'. The reality of the Project, with its hordes of desperate beggars seduced by the illusion, is 'a nightmare posing as a dream'.

Yet Deb does not condemn this. As his protagonist observes, 'appearances and illusions are important everywhere', but especially 'in a place where illusions mask an unbearable reality'. Such 'necessary' illusions make life tolerable. The rickshaw drivers who hide their faces, ashamed of their menial status, are aware that everyone knows who they are; it is the gesture that is important. These are surfaces 'of concealment', necessary in a world where everyone wears masks to 'cover the unpalatable tasks they carried out in order to carry on'. As Amrit observes, people stripped of power hold on to their few illusions all the more desperately. The counterfeit banknotes funding Malik's activities paradoxically impart 'a degree of authenticity' lacking in the dirty, disintegrating originals. This is a 'bewildering world where fulfilment and failure often appeared in the same guise'.

Finally, Amrit does write his version – 'finished', but not necessarily 'complete' of what happened to Leela, the girl in the photograph, carefully edited to conceal his true feelings. He enquires, 'do we always want to finish a story, or do we prefer to stop at a point where the story still makes sense to us?' This is a key question in a novel about the creation of fiction. Amrit finds himself in situations 'without knowing' how he got there. He is aware of his own passivity, if not his functionality. He knows that 'too many unlikely events' have come together, but he cannot know why. Patterns, mirror-images, repetitions, opposites and doubles abound: Malik's wife, flanked by two masked rickshaw riders, is another version of Leela's photograph. Amrit discovers that he and Leela were in Delhi at the same time, 'circling each other without ever quite meeting, creating a pattern whose meaning would have eluded us had we ever been aware of it'.

There are literary patterns too. Malik's parallels with Conrad's protagonist Marlow are clear, and thematically too *Surface* echoes the concerns of *Heart of Darkness*. But there are other literary references, mirrored, distorted or subverted, as in the appearance of the novelist Graham Greene, or the Victorian fiction where Amrit reads of different possibilities. One of Deb's epigraphs is from *Heart of Darkness*: 'Do you see the story? Do you see anything?' And here there are many stories – including the story of India itself. Unlike Amrit's physical journey, however, the intellectual journey is so well signposted that one is compelled to wonder whether this is merely superficial profundity. Perhaps the novel has illusions of grandeur, or perhaps 'it is necessary to conceal surfaces under other surface' – in which case it is profoundly superficial. As always, the reader must decide.

Margaret Beveridge

The Inheritance of Loss
Kiran Desai. Hamish Hamilton. ISBN 0241143489. £16.99

The past has been called another country. For Kiran Desai, its border with the present is as porous as the one between Nepal and India. Set in north-east India in the 1980s at the time of the Nepalese insurgency, *The Inheritance of Loss* evokes an unfixed landscape of past, its contours unstable, fluid. (Incidentally, Desai has been vilified as 'colonial' and 'prejudiced' in the Nepalese press.)

In a question that could have been framed by Lewis Carroll for Alice, a character asks: 'But what is in the past remains unchanged, doesn't it?' The answer carries the certitude only of uncertainty: 'I think it does change. The present changes the past. Looking back, you do not find what you left behind…' This realisation is just one expression of the inheritance of loss.

The mood is unhurried, conjectural, the structure associative. From the opening sequence, which finds sixteen-year-old Sai reading about giant squids in one of her grandfather's old *National Geographic* magazines, Desai establishes a shimmering atmosphere, almost as if events are happening under water – although the damp, mist-wreathed town Kalimpong is so far above sea level. Kanchenjunga is strangely personified in young Sai's consciousness. The mountain, both familiar and mythic, is somehow reminiscent of a giant squid. As she looks up at it, we sense with her the magnitude of time, the mysteries of the Earth's cycles and its many physical guises. Sai has learned that ammonites have been found on Everest and she mulls over the idea that that the world's highest mountain was once covered by sea – just one of the many ways that Desai raises the idea of impermanence.

Impermanence is materially embodied in the collapsed elegance of the house where Sai lives with her grandfather (a retired judge) and his cook. Perched on the mountainside, mouldering a little more with each heavy fall of rain, a decaying colonial relic riddled with damp, efflorescing with colourful fungal growths. It is abode to colonies of insects: termite tracks cover the furniture and everything that takes place under its roof is witnessed by thousands of spiders. Signalling its return to nature, snakes are emboldened to slither across the patio right up to the door.

The judge's spirit is musty with regret and confounded hopes. The reasons for his bitterness gradually emerge: the experience of leaving India to study law in England, the fractured identity this brings, his return to an arranged marriage with a woman he doesn't know, his snobbery and descent into violence towards her. Finally, there is the poignancy of her social placelessness after he returns her to her family. Unknown to both of them, she is already pregnant.

He might never again have to wince with disgust at the way she eats or the fact that she squats on the seat of his flushing lavatory; instead, he experiences the invasion of a horrible understanding of self, without a whit of redemption. He may understand that his decision to shelter his grandchild represents a subconscious impulse to make amends, but there is no comfort to be had in this knowledge, no release from his vicious ill-temper.

At the core of *The Inheritance of Loss* is the blighted love affair of Sai and her mathematics tutor, Gyan. There are delightfully humorous moments – 'he was forced to shout over the sound of rain on the tin roof, which imparted an epic quality to geometry that was clearly ridiculous' – but the light-hearted eroticism of their courtship is swiftly overtaken by political events. Only a few years her senior, Gyan joins the Gorkha Liberation Front and tells his brothers-in-arms about the rusty old rifle at the judge's house. The resultant raid provides the novel's opening scene, threat descending into farce as the bandits show their contempt for the decrepit fixtures and fittings.

Inheritance of loss and indeed loss of inheritance manifest in many ways, from the haunting image of irises carved in stone by the Mughals, to the struggles and aspirations of migrants, to the nationalistic dreams of the insurgent Nepalese. The following description of a journey to Sikkhim in the 1950s encapsulates the qualities that won Kiran Desai the Man Booker Prize:

In the rainy season, leeches would free-fall from the trees onto us, timing precisely the perfect acrobat moment. We would wash in saltwater to keep them off, salt our shoes and socks, even our hair. The storms would wash the salt off and we'd have to stop and salt ourselves again. The forests at that time were fierce and enormous – if you were told a magical beast lived there, you'd believe it. We'd emerge to the tops of mountains where monasteries limpet to sides of rock, surrounded by chortens and prayer flags, the white facades catching the light of the sunset, all straw gold, the mountains rugged lines of indigo.

Desai, resident in the US since her teenage years, is taking a creative writing course at Columbia University. Nevertheless, she told the *Times of India* following the publication of her first novel, *Hullabaloo in the Guava Orchard*: 'There are all kinds of theories that you get told in writing workshops – "Write what you know" and that sort of thing, which I don't believe at all. I think one of the great joys of writing is to try and explore what you don't know…'

Jennie Renton

They Scream When You Kill Them
Des Dillon. Luath Press. ISBN 1905222351. £7.99

They Scream When You Kill Them is a collection of twenty-eight short stories, set for the most part in Glasgow and Galloway, where Des Dillon now makes his home. The subject matter may be summarised under three broad themes: violence, animals and alcohol.

Dillon's vision of contemporary Glasgow is a form of urban nightmare. The threat of violence is never far away. Neds lurk menacingly on almost every street corner. Reminiscent of *The Glasgow Dragon* (2004), his novel about drugs and the criminal underworld, many of these stories operate at the level of reportage. There is a reluctance to judge either the perpetrators of such violence or the social system that has nurtured this type of behaviour. 'Soap Opera' examines the voyeuristic mentality of contemporary culture, with people posing at a bus queue in order to watch a violent domestic unfold in front of them. At times the narrative becomes unconvincing in its unflinching attempts to plumb the depths of human depravity. 'Jif Lemons' tells of two friends who attempt to escape the city by going to the Highlands on a fishing trip. Their pastoral retreat is interrupted by the unexplained arrival of three men, who subject a girl to a horrific gang rape before producing a chainsaw and attempting to murder the fishermen. At moments like this, Dillon's stories take on a tabloid feel. They seem content to represent social breakdown, to dwell pruriently on it, without attempting the kind of interrogation that characterises the work of say, William McIlvanney. These kinds of narrative are offset, puzzlingly one might argue, by a series of stories centred on animals. Cats and dogs, rather than people, form the object of the collection's greatest affection.

'They Scream When You Kill Them' refers to the noise langoustines make when you boil them. In this story, the narrator and his wife cannot go through with the deed and are compelled to release the creatures back to the sea. Alcohol, or rather alcoholism, provides a bridge between Dillon's writing and one of the most recurring motifs of Scottish literature. In a new take on a familiar theme, *They Scream When You Kill Them* focuses on the experience of individuals involved in Alcoholics Anonymous. Several stories explore the challenges involved in attempting to live with addiction, and it is here they reach their most insightful and compassionate pitch.

Matthew McGuire

Notes on Contributors

Shanta Acharya was born in Orissa, India, and educated at St Joseph's Convent School and Ravenshaw College, Cuttack, where she completed her Master of Arts and subsequently served as a Lecturer in English. In 1979 she went to Oxford University, where she completed her doctoral thesis in 1983. Between 1983 and 1985, she was a Visiting Scholar, as well as Teaching-cum-Research Assistant, at Harvard University. In 1985 she moved to London and began her investment management career with Morgan Stanley Asset Management. www.shantaacharya.com

Hannah Adcock is a freelance writer who has been commissioned to write articles for both the national and regional press. Her first book, *Twentysomething: The Ultimate Survival Guide* (Discover Press, 2004) was published when she was twenty-three. A graduate of Cambridge University, Hannah was keen to undertake research from original source material and Miss Plumb proved a compelling study. Hannah's main areas of interest are history, books, secondhand bookshops and budget travel.

Anjana Basu has had a book of short stories published by Orient Longman, India, and her poems have featured in an anthology brought out by Penguin India. The BBC has broadcast one of her short stories. In America she has been published in *Gowanus*, *The Blue Moon Review*, and *Recursive Angel*, to name a few. In Canada her work has appeared in the *Antigonish Review*. In 2003, Harper Collins brought out her novel *Curses In Ivory* and IndiaInk will soon be bringing out *Black Tongue*, her second novel. In 2004 she was a Hawthornden Fellow.

Margaret Burnett lives in Edinburgh and teaches English as a foreign language. She has published a novel, *Indians Don't Kiss*, and short stories in magazines. Born in Pakistan and brought up in India, she has learned to love Scotland and nothing delights her more than sitting in a cottage in Skye and writing about India.

Rajorshi Chakraborti lives between Calcutta and Edinburgh, where he teaches Literature and Creative Writing part-time at the university. His first novel, *Or the Day Seizes You*, was published by Penguin India early this year, and should be available for wider release sometime next year. In the meantime he has completed a second novel, *Derangements*, and another novella. 'In Economy' forms the opening of his latest work, which will be a sequel to his first book.

Swapan Chakravorty is Professor and Head, Department of English, Jadavpur University, Kolkata. His books include *Society and Politics in the Plays of Thomas Middleton* (Oxford: Clarendon Press, 1996) and *Bangalir ingreji sahityacharcha* (Kolkata: Anustup, 2006). He has co-edited *Print Areas: Book History in India* (Delhi: Permanent Black, 2004), and is contributory editor, *Collected Works of Thomas Middleton* (Oxford: Oxford University Press, forthcoming).

Sangeeta Datta is a film historian and filmmaker. Her documentaries *The Way I See It* (on women filmakers in India) and *In Search of Durga* (on Bengali diaspora and culture) have received critical attention, showcased in several film festivals and used in curriculum. Datta's monograph on Shyam Benegal has been published by the British Film Institute as part of World Directors Series. She works regularly with British Museum and National Film Theatre on film events and programmes. In Spring 2007 she will teach a post-graduate course on South Asian Visual culture at the University of London, Centre for English Studies. Her short film *Letter from an Ordinary Girl* has been screened to great acclaim at the Voices of Bengal festival in the British Museum. She has worked with Rituparno Ghosh as Associate Director for Chokher Bali, Raincoat and Antarmahal.

Dr Bashabi Fraser is an academic and writer based in Edinburgh. She is an Honorary Fellow at the Centre for South Asian Studies, Edinburgh University and an Associate Lecturer in English Literature and Creative Writing at the Open University in Scotland and the West Midlands. Her interests cover post-colonial literature and literary theory, focusing on related themes like culture, identity, dislocation, relocation, diaspora, memory, nostalgia and creativity and her writing and research, traverse her eastern heritage and western experience, moving between and combining her two worlds. Recent publications include: *Bengal Partition Stories: An Unclosed Chapter* (London: Anthem Press, 2006), *A Meeting of Two Minds: Geddes-Tagore Letters* (Edinburgh: Word Power Books, Revised edition, 2005), and *Tartan & Turban*, a collection of poetry (Edinburgh: Luath Press, 2004).

Merryn Glover was born in Kathmandu and grew up in Nepal, India and Pakistan. After a teaching degree in Australia she moved to Scotland, working in community arts, before returning to Nepal to teach at an international school. She now lives with her husband and two sons at the foot of the Cairngorms and dreams of Asia.

Martin Goodman writes novels, non-fiction, and plays as well as teaching creative writing. His latest novel *Slippery When Wet* (Transita, 1996) is typical of his writing in the way it crosses many boundaries. 'India, by Design' is one of a sequence of stories featuring Arnold, at seven year stages. This one draws on travels featured in Martin's book *On Sacred Mountains*, particularly visits to the holy Indian mountain of Arunachala. Coming later in 2007 are *Mentoring for Creative Writers*, an Arts Council project fronted by New Writing North and co-authored with Sara Maitland, and a biography of J.S. Haldane.

Jane Griffiths was born in Devon, but brought up in Holland. She has taught at Oxford, and also worked as a bookbinder and lexicographer. She was the recipient of an Eric Gregory Award in 1996, and her two books of poetry (*A Grip on Thin Air* and *Icarus on Earth*) are published by Bloodaxe. She has also published a study of the Tudor poet John Skelton with OUP.

Anjum Katyal works as an editor in the field of the arts, including cinema, theatre, fine arts and culture studies. She also writes poetry, sings the blues, and does the occasional translation. She is a Calcuttan by choice and upbringing.

Naveen Kishore works as a publisher for Seagull Books (Calcutta). He is also a lighting designer, graphic designer, photographer and documentary filmmaker.

Usha Kishore Born in Kerala, South India, Usha Kishore now lives on the Isle of Man, where she lectures in English at the Isle of Man College. Usha's poetry has been published in magazines and anthologies in the US, UK, Ireland, Europe, NZ and India. She also writes critical articles, which have appeared in international magazines. Her short story 'Dowry' was shortlisted for the Asham Award (UK), 2005.

Kenny Munro Freelance arts educator, enabler and sculptor. many of his civic sculptures were inspired by the Geddes Grid 'thinking machines'; projects in schools examine environmental themes, sustainable transport issues and relationships between communities in Scotland, France, Australia and India. He was chairman of Edinburgh Sculpture Workshop, 1997–2000. His sculptural homage to Sir Patrick Geddes, a granite and bronze pillar entitled 'Evergreen', can be viewed at Rodney Garden, on the river walkway in Perth. He collaborated in The Stones of Scotland, conceived with George Wyllie MBE and Lesley-May Miller: a 'sculpture for democracy', this circle of thirty-two stones, with poetry by Hugh MacDiarmid and Tessa Ransford, overlooks the Scottish Parliament. www.kennymunrosculpture.com

Gurcharan Rampuri has been writing poetry in Punjabi for well over five decades. Author of seven volumes of poetry, he moved to Vancouver, British Columbia, in 1964. He has won many awards, and his poems have been translated into many languages, including Russian, Hindi, Gujarati, and English. His *Collected Poems* has recently appeared in India. Many of his lyrical poems have been set to music and sung by well-known singers such as Surinder Kaur and Jagjit Zirvi.

Judy Ray co-edited, with David Ray, Fathers: A Collection of Poems (St Martin's Press). Her recent chapbooks are *Sleeping in the Larder: Poems of a Sussex Childhood* and *Fishing in Green Waters*. Earlier publications include *Pigeons in the Chandeliers* and a prose memoir, The Jaipur Sketchbook: Impressions of India. She is a volunteer teacher of English to adults in the community in Tucson.

Shampa Ray was born in New Delhi. An artist and writer, her poetry has been published in various magazines – *Spectrum, Fox* and *Textualities*, and anthologies – *Wish I Was Here* (pocketbooks) and *Rising Fire* (Friends of the Western Buddhist Order). She lives in Edinburgh. Her main influences are Buddhism and art.

Sudeep Sen is the 2004 recipient of the prestigious 'Pleiades' honour at the world's oldest poetry festival – the Struga Poetry Evenings, Macedonia – for having made 'significant contribution to modern world poetry'. Sen studied at St Columba's School and read literature at Delhi University and in the USA. As an Inlaks Scholar, he completed an MS from the Graduate School of Journalism at Columbia University in New York. Winner of many international and national prizes, he was awarded a Hawthornden Fellowship (UK) and nominated for a Pushcart Prize (USA) for poems included in *Postmarked India: New & Selected Poems* (HarperCollins). More recently, he has published *Postcards from Bangladesh*, *Prayer Flag, Distracted Geographies*, and *Rain*. As an invited author representing his country, he has read his work worldwide, and has been translated into numerous languages. Sen was an international poet-in-residence at the Scottish Poetry Library in Edinburgh and a visiting scholar at Harvard University. He is the editor of *Atlas*, editorial director of Aark Arts, and lives in New Delhi and London. www.sudeepsen.net.

Amritjit Singh is Langston Hughes Professor of English at Ohio University in Athens, Ohio. A Series Editor for the MELA (Multi-Ethnic Literatures of the Americas) Series from Rutgers University Press, he has authored or co-edited well over a dozen books on American, postcolonial and South Asian literatures, including *Postcolonial Theory and the United States: Race, Ethnicity, Literature* (2000); *The Collected Writings of Wallace Thurman* (2003); and *Interviews with Edward W. Said* (2004).

Subscribe to *Edinburgh Review*

Individual subscriptions (3 issues annually) £17 / $27 / 27 Euros
Institutional subscriptions (3 issues annually) £34 / $54 / 54 Euros

Please complete and return this subscription form to *Edinburgh Review*, 22a Buccleuch Place, Edinburgh, EH8 9LN.

Back Issues are available at £5. Please contact our office for availability information or to place an order.

Subscription Form

Name:

Address:

Postcode:

I wish to subscribe to *Edinburgh Review*, beginning from issue _____.
I enclose payment for £17 (individual) / £34 (institutional)*
[* = delete as applicable]

Please make cheques payable to '*Edinburgh Review*'.

To pay by Credit / Debit Card, please complete details below:

Type of Card: VISA / Mastercard / Switch [delete as appropriate]

Card Number : _____ _____ _____ _____

Card Valid from : __ / __ / __ to : __ / __ / __ Issue No : __ [Switch only]

Signature : _____ Date : __ / __ / __